# Developing Music Skills

## Grades K-3

**Written by Linda Ann Hopley**
**Illustrated by S&S Learning Materials**

**About the author:**
Linda Ann Hopley has been a piano and theory teacher for over 30 years. She has written material for music for the last ten years. She loves working with children and helping them to develop an interest and appreciation for music.

 "We acknowledge the financial support of the Government of Canada through the Book Publishing Industry Development Program (BPIDP) for this project."



Published in the United States by:
On the Mark Press
P.O. Box 433
Clayton, New York
13624
www.onthemarkpress.com

Published in Canada by:
S&S Learning Materials
15 Dairy Avenue
Napanee, Ontario
K7R 1M4
www.sslearning.com

ISBN: 9781554950843 

# At A Glance Kindergarten

| Learning Expectations | The Musical Alphabet | The Keyboard | Instruments in a Band | The Marching Beat | Notes | Rests | The Treble Clef | The Bass Clef | The Singing Scale | The Composer | The Conductor | Music Memory Game | Review and Quiz |
|---|---|---|---|---|---|---|---|---|---|---|---|---|---|
| **Understanding Concepts** | | | | | | | | | | | | | |
| • Learning the 7 letters in music. | • | | | | | | | | | | | • | |
| • Learning how to print music. | • | | | | | | | | | | | | |
| • Learning about groups of black keys on the keyboard. | | • | | | | | | | | | | | |
| • Learning about sounds that instruments make. | | • | • | | | | | | | | | | |
| • Learning about the difference between notes and rests. | | | | | • | • | | | | | | | • |
| • Learning about shapes. | | | | | • | • | | | | | | | |
| • Learning to count. | | | | • | • | | | | | | | | |
| • Learning about pitch. | | | | | | | • | • | • | | | | |
| • Learning the difference between composers and conductors. | | | | | | | | | | • | • | | |
| • Learning about beats. | | | • | • | | | | | | | | | |
| **Skills of Inquiry, Design, and Communication** | | | | | | | | | | | | | |
| • Creativity | • | • | • | • | • | • | • | • | • | • | • | • | • |
| • Counting, marching, singing. | | | | • | • | | | | • | | | | |
| • Working within a group. | optional | | | | | | | | | | | • | • |
| • Relating music to the outside world. | | | • | | | | | | | • | • | | • |

ISBN: 9781554950843

| Learning Expectations | Percussion Instruments | The One - Beat Note | The One - Beat Rest | The Staff | The Treble Clef | A B C D E F G | Do, Re, Mi, Fa, Sol, La, Ti, Do | High and Low Pitch | The Composer | Music Reviews With Games, Quizzes, and Songs |
|---|---|---|---|---|---|---|---|---|---|---|
| **Understanding Concepts** | | | | | | | | | | |
| • Understanding shapes. | • | | | • | | • | | | | |
| • Learning the letters used in music. | • | | | | | • | | • | | • |
| • Understanding what one beat is. | • | • | • | | | | | | | • |
| • Learning what gets one beat. | | • | • | | | | | | | • |
| • Learning about high and low notes. | • | | | | | | • | • | | • |
| • Recognizing the treble clef and what music is written on. | | | | | • | | | | | • |
| • Recognizing percussion instruments and learning how they work. | • | | | | | | | | | • |
| • Learning about a composer. | • | | | | | | | | • | • |
| **Skills of Inquiry, Design, and Communication** | | | | | | | | | | |
| • Creativity | • | • | • | • | • | • | • | • | • | • |
| • Working within a group. | • | optional | | | | | | | | • |
| • Counting and adding. | • | | • | • | | | • | | | • |
| • Recognition of letters. | • | | | | • | • | | | | • |
| • Relating music to the outside world. | | | | | | | | | • | • |

**Grade 2**

| Learning Expectations | String Instruments | The Difference Betweem 1 or 2 Beats | The Two Beat Note | The Two Beat Rest | The Bar Line and Double Bar Line | The Bass Clef | The Difference Between Treble and Bass | A B C D E F G | Do, Re, Mi, Fa, Sol, La, Ti, Do | The Composer Mozart | Music Reviews |
|---|---|---|---|---|---|---|---|---|---|---|---|
| **Understanding Concepts** | | | | | | | | | | | |
| • Learning the letters used in music. | • | | | | | | | • | | | • |
| • Understanding what one beat is. | • | • | | | | | • | | | | • |
| • Learning about two beats. | • | • | • | • | | | • | | | | • |
| • Learning about high and low notes. | | | | | | • | | | • | | • |
| • Recognizing the difference between treble and bass. | | • | • | • | | • | • | | | | • |
| • Learning about the staff, bar lines, and double bar lines. | • | | | | • | | | | | | • |
| • Learning about string instruments. | | • | • | • | | | | | | | |
| • Learning about one half and one quarter. | • | | | | | | | | | | • |
| • Learning about a composer. | | | | | | | | | | • | |
| • Learning what a solo or duet is. | • | | | | | | | | | | |
| **Skills of Inquiry and Communication** | | | | | | | | | | | |
| • Creativity | • | • | • | • | • | • | • | • | • | • | • |
| • Working with others. | • | ------------- optional ------------- | | | | | | | | | • |
| • Counting and adding. | • | • | • | • | | | | | | | • |
| • Recognition of letters. | | | | | | | | • | | | • |
| • Relating music to the outside world. | • | • | | | | | • | | | • | • |

ISBN: 9781554950843

# At A Glance Grade 3

| Learning Expectations | Woodwind Instruments | The Difference Between 1, 2, and 3 Beats | The One Beat Note and Rest | The Two Beat Note and Rest | The Three Beat Note | Pitch and the Difference Between Treble & Bass | The Brace | Pitch Difference Between Brace & Quarter Note | The Staff, Bar Line, and Double Bar Line | Repeat Signs | The Composer Beethoven | A B C D E F G, Do to Do, and Pitch | Music Reviews |
|---|---|---|---|---|---|---|---|---|---|---|---|---|---|
| **Understanding Concepts** | | | | | | | | | | | | | |
| • Learning about a composer. | | | | | | | | | | | • | | • |
| • Recognizing woodwind instruments. | • | | | | | | | | | | | | • |
| • Understanding what one beat is. | | • | • | | | | | | | | | | • |
| • Learning what gets one, two, and three beats. | | • | • | • | • | | | | | | | | • |
| • Recognizing the treble and bass clef. | | | | | | • | | | | | | | |
| • Recognizing the staff and its components. | | | | | | | • | • | • | • | | | • |
| • Learning the singing scale, the music scale, and understanding pitch. | • | | | | | • | | | | | | • | • |
| **Skills of Inquiry, Design, and Communication** | | | | | | | | | | | | | |
| • Creativity | • | • | • | • | • | • | • | • | • | • | • | • | • |
| • Review of the alphabet. | • | | | | | | | | | | | | • |
| • Subtraction. | | • | • | • | • | | | | | | | | • |
| • Adding, counting, and multiplying. | | • | • | • | • | | | | | | | | • |
| • Counting by 2's and problem solving. | • | | | | | | | | | | | | |
| • Working with a group. | • | ------------ optional ------------ | | | | | | | | | • | • | • |
| • Relating music to the outside world. | | | | | | | | | | | • | | • |

# Table of Contents Kindergarten

# Table of Contents Grade 1

# Table of Contents Grade 2

# Table of Contents Grade 3

# Teacher Assessment Rubric Grades K to 3

**Student's Name:** ______________________ **Date:** ________________

| Criteria | Level 1 | Level 2 | Level 3 | Level 4 |
|---|---|---|---|---|
| **Understanding Concepts** | **limited** | **some** | **general** | **thorough** |
| • Demonstrated general understanding of music. | | | | |
| • Demonstrated understanding of instruments. | | | | |
| • Demonstrated understanding of rhythm, pitch, and sound. | | | | |
| **Ability to be Creative** | **fair** | **good** | **better** | **excellent** |
| • Worksheets show originality and variety. | | | | |
| • Answers show thoughtfulness. | | | | |
| **Shows Enthusiasm and Interest** | **fair** | **good** | **better** | **excellent** |
| • Projects are completed. | | | | |
| • Enjoyed and contributed in stories and songs. | | | | |
| • Eager to participate in games. | | | | |

**Teacher's Comments:** ______________________________________________

______________________________________________

______________________________________________

______________________________________________

# Student Self-Assessment Rubric

**Name:** ______________________________ **Date:** ______________________

Put a check mark ✓ in the box that best describes your performance.

| Expectations | My Performance | | |
|---|---|---|---|
| | Sometimes | Almost Always | Always |
| ✓ I am a good listener. | | | |
| ✓ I followed the directions. | | | |
| ✓ I stayed on task and finished on time. | | | |
| ✓ I was creative. | | | |
| ✓ I used a variety of material. | | | |
| ✓ My work was neat. | | | |
| ✓ I am familiar with some music signs. | | | |
| ✓ I know the names of most musical instruments. | | | |
| ✓ I know things about composers. | | | |

✓ I liked ____________________________________________

______________________________________________________

✓ I learned __________________________________________

______________________________________________________

Teacher Notes:

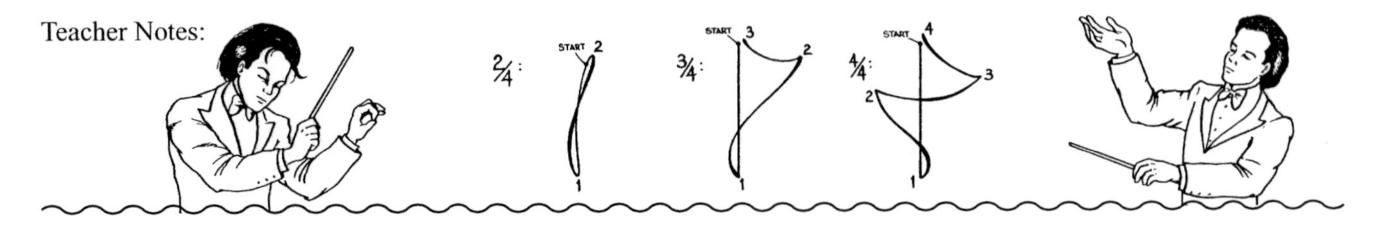


# Developing Music Skills in Kindergarten

**Introduction:**

The activities in this book have three intentions:

- to encourage students to be creative.
- to encourage their enjoyment of music.
- to educate them in the field of music.

Since creativity is very important in music, there will be variety in the way the work will be accomplished. The students should enjoy this program and take a positive approach to music. They may like to take the information home or to other environments. Music is everywhere and is a universal language. The students might be amazed at the effect it has on people's lives and the endless variety of music that exists.

1. Each exercise will have a main point or idea, a sign to learn or a musical activity to finish.

2. If there are small dots, the student is to connect the dots to help them form letters, numbers, signs or directions.

3. A variety of materials are encouraged such as crayons, markers, colored paper or other available supplies.

4. The students could make a booklet for music reference.

5. When their booklet or amount of knowledge and activities are complete, the students should receive a certificate with or without testing, depending on the teacher.

6. The games will help the student to remember the letters in a fun atmosphere.

7. A prize board is a great incentive but is optional.

8. The concepts learned are
   - the letters used in music
   - the singing scale do to do (pronounced like dough)
   - the keyboard
   - the terms - note, rest, beat, treble clef, bass clef
   - musical instruments
   - the conductor
   - the composer.

Teacher Notes:

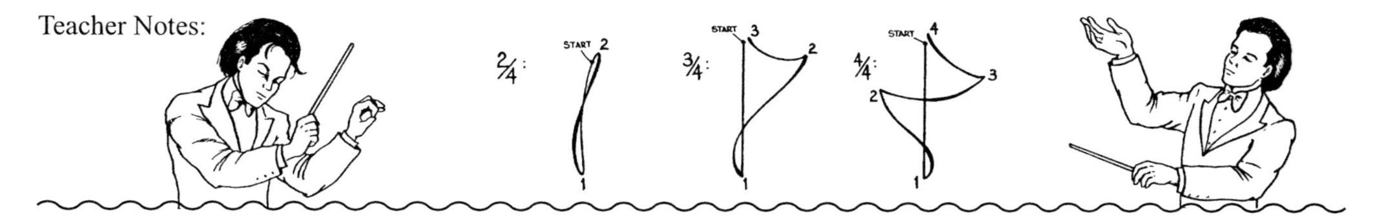


# List of Materials

- Worksheets will be completed with a variety of coloring materials.
- Crayons of different textures and colors, markers or pencil crayons of different shades are very effective.
- Graphite pencils will be needed for drawing.
- For the suggested instruments in the rhythm band, you will need two sticks for all students who will be using sticks, a variety of bells to make the bell shakers, ribbon, paint, and metallic string or wool. Use hat boxes, shoe boxes or other boxes with lids to make drums.
- For the games, construction paper will be needed to back the cards. You may wish to laminate them to ensure longer use.
- The reproducibles that are to be traced (see page 56) should be mounted onto cardboard and laminated as they wear out easily. Extra copies should be made. If the reproducibles are being used for the students to trace to make different designs, they should be placed under the paper and regular crayons may be used for shading. If the reproducibles are to be traced by the students on top of the page, regular pencil crayons or pencils should be used and crayons may be used for coloring them.
- Incentives, such as prizes for a prize board, are great for encouragement. The prize board would have to be backed with construction paper or other colored background paper. Prizes could be placed on the board as rewards for good work. The prizes could include music stickers, erasers or other small items.

Teacher Notes:

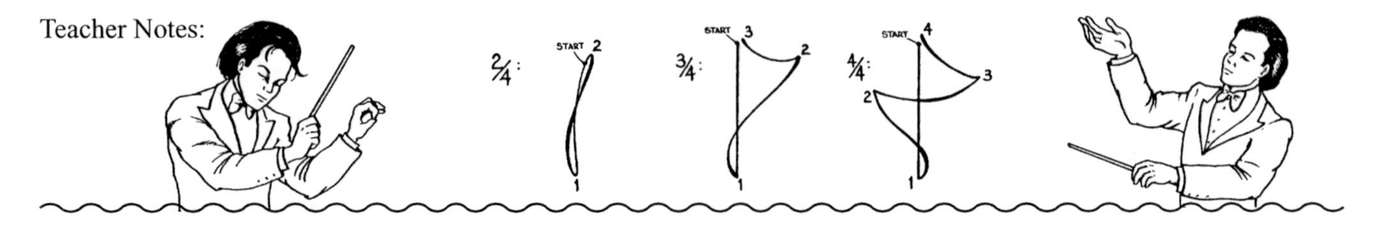


# Teaching Suggestions

- Be familiar with the music terms at this level.
- Try having the children work individually, in groups or as a class.
- If working in groups, rotate them at different work stations.
- Different textured crayons work great and go a long way while completing the worksheets.
- Make the instruments before doing the songs as the students may want to play along.
- Students with some knowledge of music should be grouped with students who do not have any knowledge of music.
- Assemble games and boards ahead of time. Make extra copies of game pieces or stencils as needed.
- Teach the students how to play the games.
- Encourage the students to think of music at home and in other environments.
- If possible, bring instruments into the classroom. A talent show may be of interest to the students.
- Encourage creativity and enjoyment at all times.

Teacher Notes:

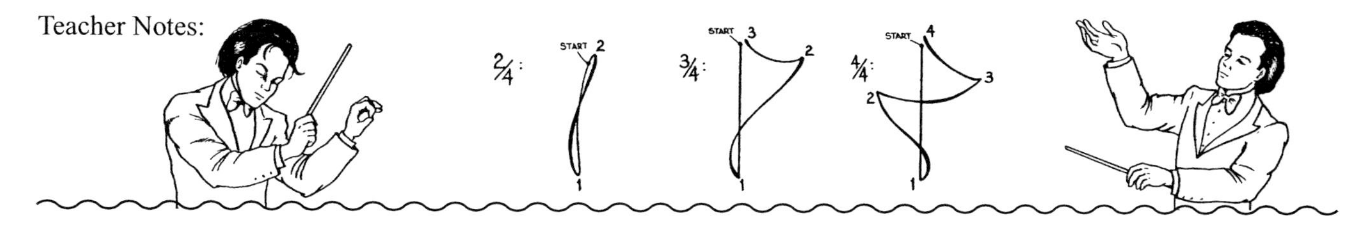


# Music Glossary

**Notes:** When you see a note, there needs to be a sound made by an instrument or voice.

**Rests:** Rests are periods of silence.

**One Beat:** One beat is one count, like the tick of a clock. When resting for one beat, there needs to be a period of silence for the count of one.

**High and Low Pitch:** Some instruments play in a higher range or pitch just like some voices have a higher range or pitch. The high range uses the treble clef and the low range uses the bass clef. For some voicing or instruments in between these ranges, the alto and tenor clefs are used.

**Treble Clef:** The treble clef is used for the highest pitched instruments and voices or the higher end of keyboard instruments. The middle point of the treble clef centers all round the "G" line of the staff and sometimes can be called the "G clef."

**Bass Clef:** The bass clef is used for the lowest instruments or the low end of the keyboard. The bass clef circles around the "F" line and is sometimes called the "F clef."

**Composer:** A composer is a song-writer from the past or present.

**Conductor:** A conductor directs the music of an orchestra or a choir using a wand or sometimes his/her hand.

**The Music Scale:** The music scale consists of the letters A, B, C, D, E, F, and G.

**The Singing Scale:** The singing scale consists of the words do, re, mi, fa, sol, la, ti, and high do.

**The Keyboard:** The Keyboard is a set of keys consisting of white keys and groups of black keys. They are in groups of two and three. The piano keyboard centers around middle "C," which is before the group of two black keys

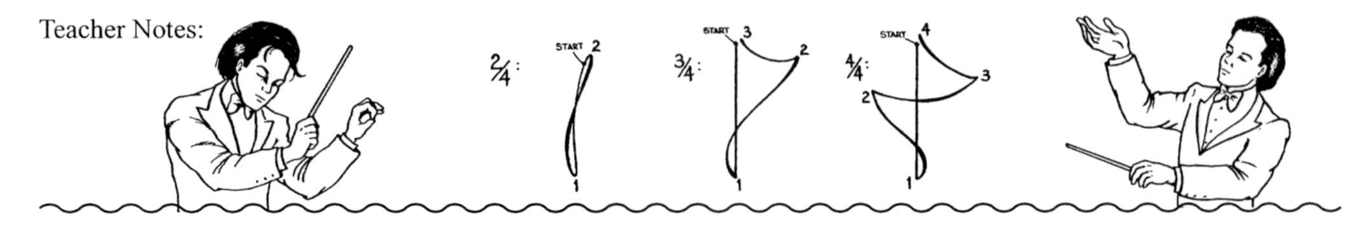


# Music Incentives

- The Music Incentives
- The Music Scale A, B, C, D, E, F, and G
- The Singing Scale Do to Do
- The Rhythm Instruments

1. The optional music incentives are ideas to encourage participation.
   A chart on a bulletin board is one suggestion. The students' names would be listed one below each other. The students would accumulate points which would be given for completed work, for at home projects or other completed activities.

   When a student reaches a reward zone, from the accumulated points, he/she would receive a reward. This chart could be done in a circular fashion so that the student would keep going round and round the board. (See the example below.)

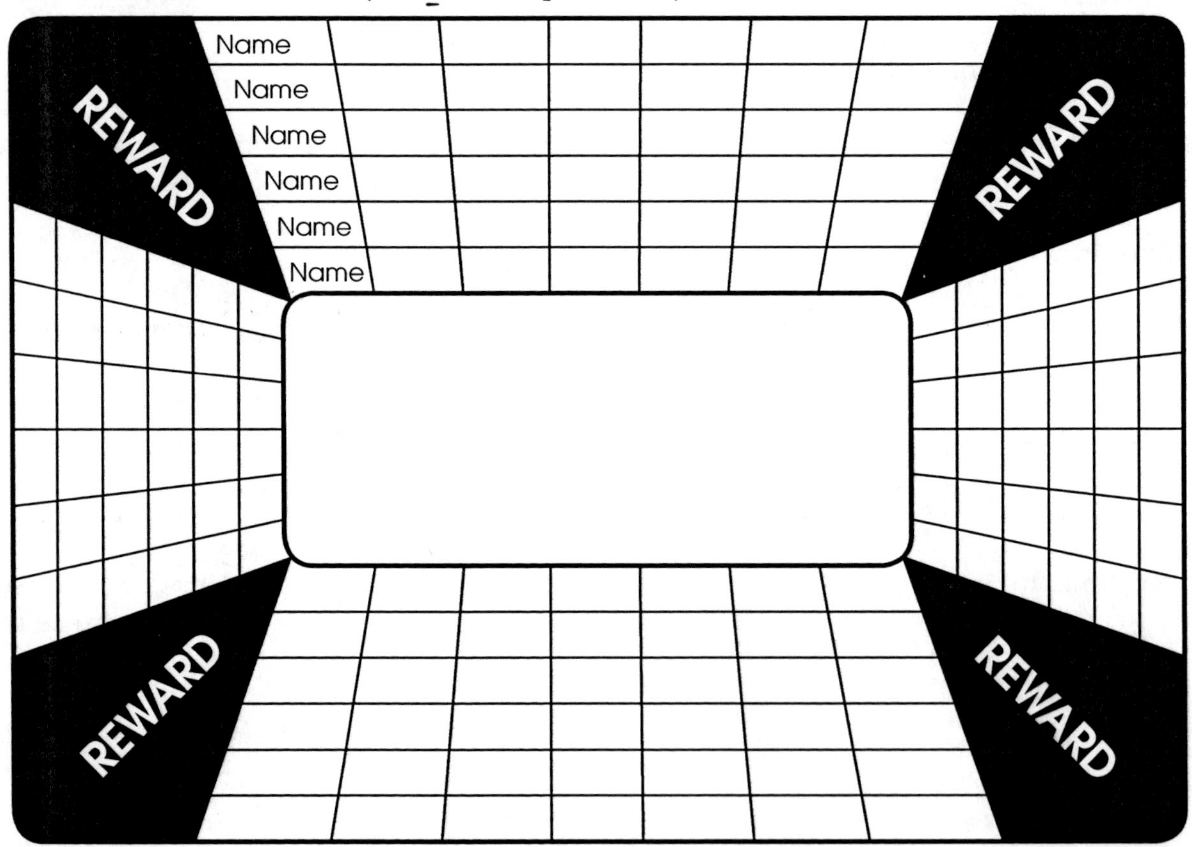


Another incentive would be a booklet in which all of the work could be kept. It would be their music book and stickers could be provided for completed work. A small incentive goes along way when it comes to music. It is something the student will pride themselves on and take home to do extra projects.

Teacher Notes:

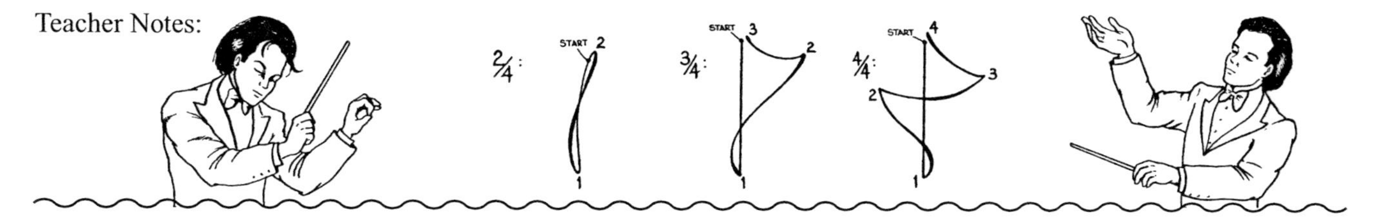


# Music Incentives

2. The game "Music Memory" is based on the seven letters of the music alphabet. This game will help students recognize the seven letters used in music. Reproduce the pages 18 to 21 to make copies of the cards to be used in the game. The letters could be mounted on a sturdy backing and then laminated to ensure longer usage. Teach the students how to play the game. Mix or shuffle the cards and place them face down on a table. Have a student choose two cards and look at them. If the two cards have different letters, the student is to return them to the table and another student has the chance to choose two cards. If the student chooses a matched pair, he/she may pick again. The player with the highest number of matching pairs wins.

3. The reproducible worksheets found on pages 22 to 29 are based on the seven letters used in music. The dotted lettering should be connected. This will help the students to learn how to spell the word music. The other activities will help the students to associate things that begin with these seven letters.

4. The worksheet on page 30 deals with the singing scale. The Do to do (pronounced dough) singing scale goes from a low to a high pitch.

5. The songs on pages 31 and 32 are based on the playing scale and the singing scale.

6. Information on how to develop a rhythm band and how to make the instruments is found on page 33. These instruments could also be involved during singing periods.

Cut out, mount, and laminate the Music Memory Cards.
Store them in an envelope and attach the instruction card.
Teach the children how to play the game.

# A Musical Letters Memory Game

1. Mix up the cards.
2. Line the cards up face down.
3. Pick up two cards and look at them.
4. If the cards look the same you can keep them and try again. You can keep trying until the pair does not match.
5. If the cards do not look the same you must return them face down to the table.
6. The next student takes a turn.

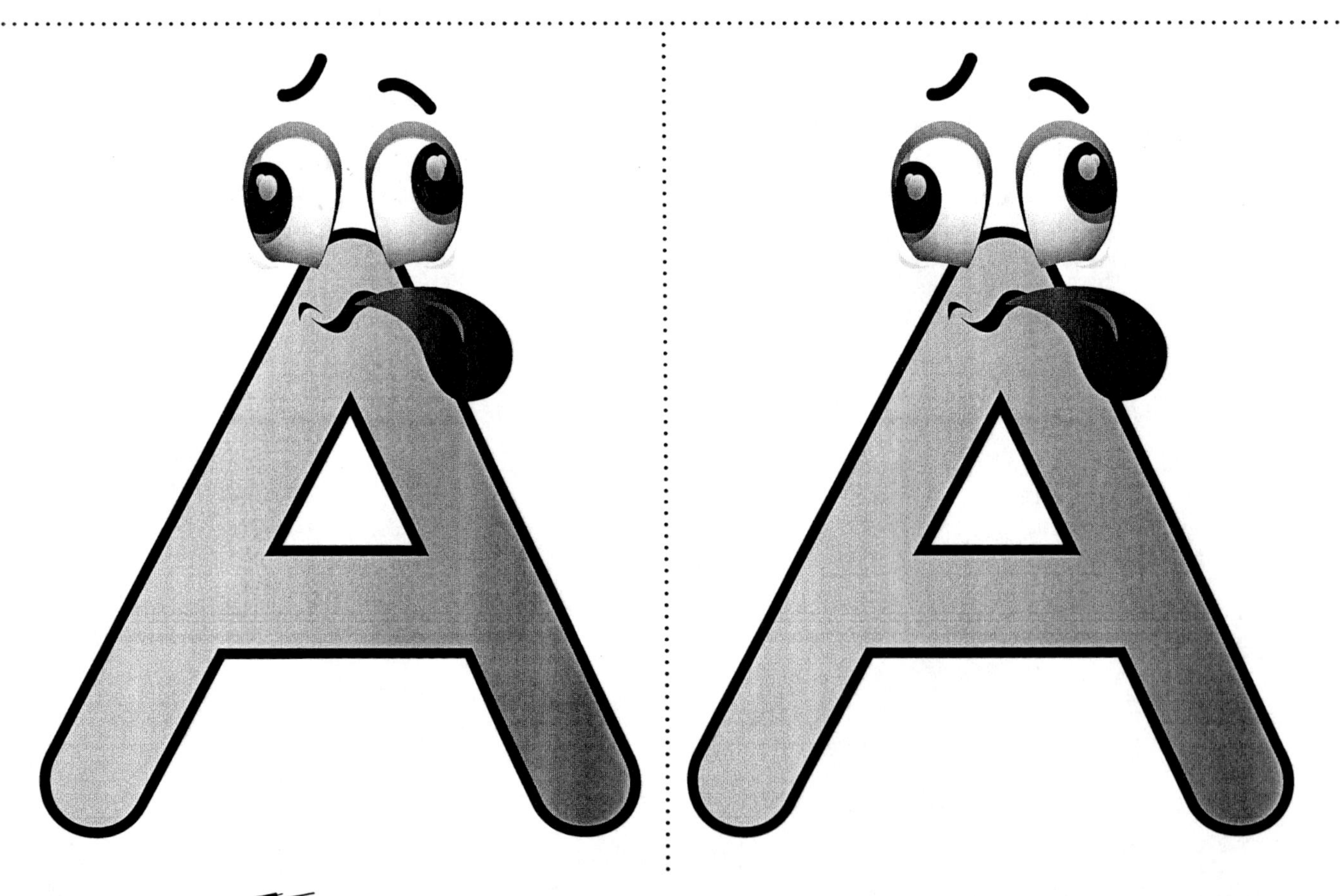

D

D

E

E

Color number 7, the word MUSIC and the A, B, C, D, E, F, G letters.

Make some more A, B, C, D, E, F, and G letters all over the screen.

THERE ARE

7

LETTERS USED

IN MUSIC.

THEY ARE

A, B, C, D, E, F, G.

Connect the dots. Color the letter and the picture.
Draw more apples.

A

Color the blocks and draw something made of blocks.
Can you count the blocks?

# B IS A LETTER USED IN MUSIC.

MANY BLOCKS

Draw more holes in the cheese.
Draw something that eats cheese.

# C IS A LETTER USED IN MUSIC.

1 BLOCK OF CHEESE

ISBN: 9781554950843 

How many bunnies do you see? ___________
How many drum sticks do you see? ___________
Draw the rest of the parade.

# D IS A LETTER USED IN MUSIC.

2

DRUMS

ISBN: 9781554950843

Some people eat eggs for breakfast.
Draw what you like to eat for breakfast.

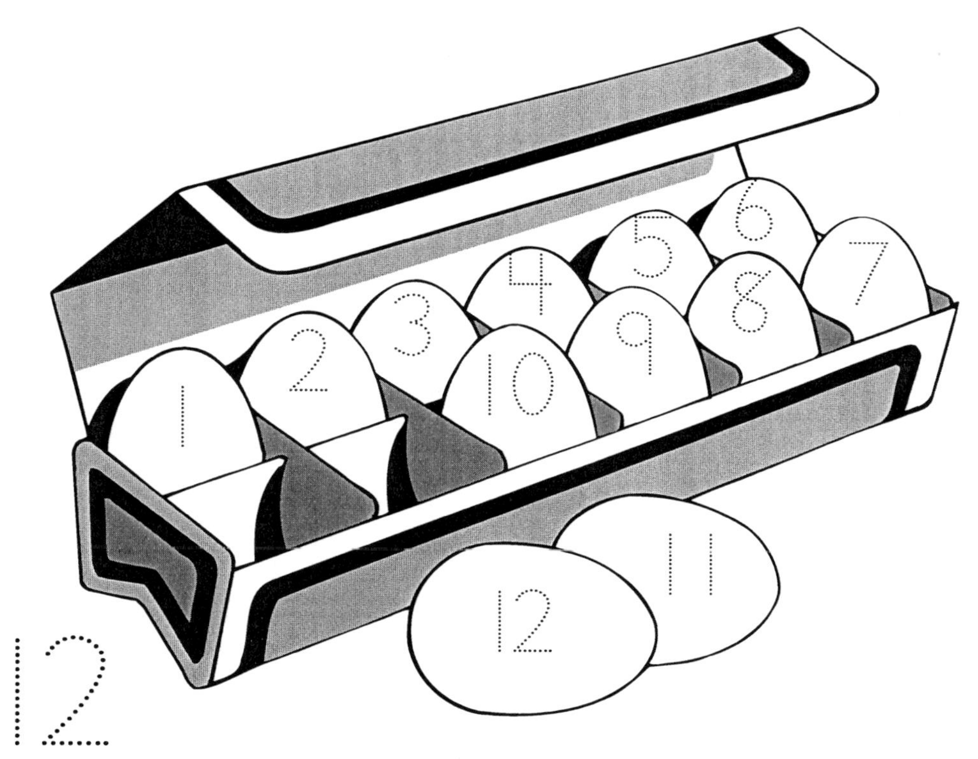


12

EGGS

Draw a picture of something that starts with the letter F.

Draw a family of gingerbread people.

IS A LETTER
USED IN

2

GINGERBREAD PEOPLE

ISBN: 9781554950843

# AS HIGH AS DO

Color the cone according to the do to do scale. Trace the letters of each name on each part of the ice cream.

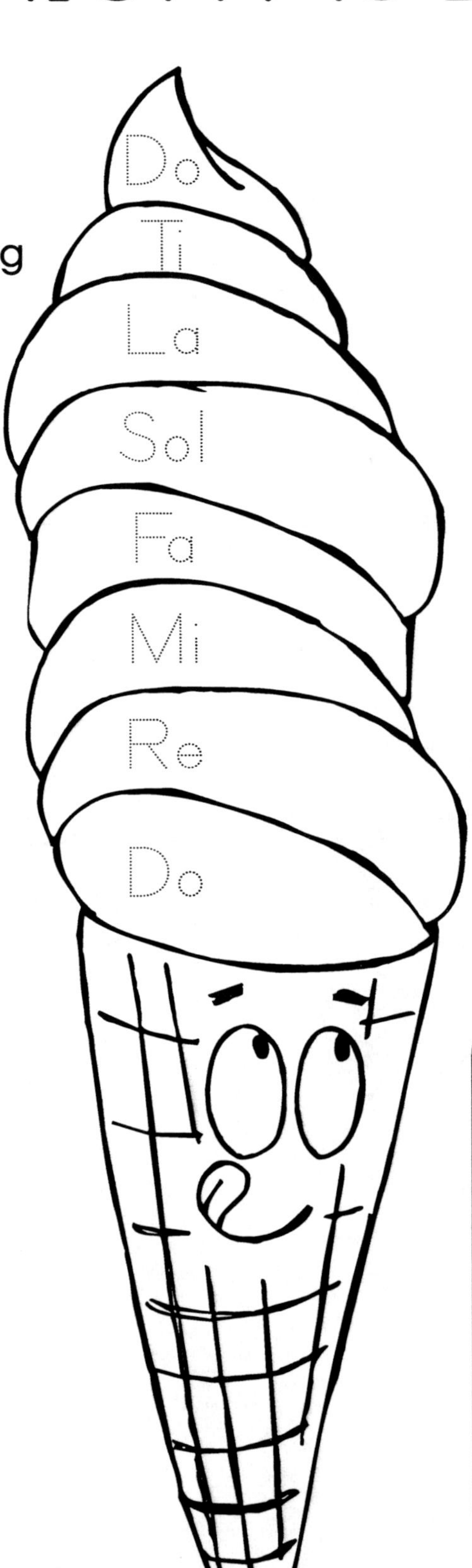


Do - cherry
Ti - chocolate
La - lemon
Sol - blueberry
Fa - lime
Mi - grape
Re - orange
Do - cherry

ISBN: 9781554950843

# FORWARDS BACKWARDS

A B C D E F G,
Is my playing scale.
G F E D C B A,
Backwards from the top.

Do, Re, Mi, Fa, Sol, La, Ti, Do,
Is my singing scale.
Do, Ti, La, Sol, Fa, Mi, Re, Do,
Backwards then we stop.

ISBN: 9781554950843

# A TO G

A is for apple and
B is for ball,
C is for candy and
D is for doll,
E is for eggs and
F is for fall,
G is for going because
That is all.

ISBN: 9781554950843

Teacher Notes:

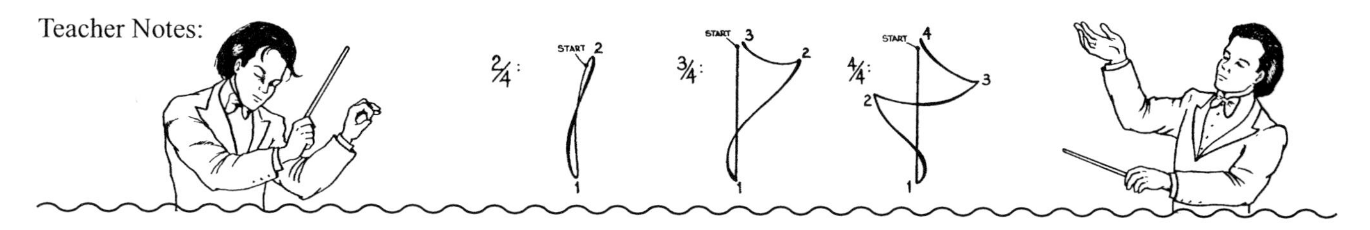


# Instruments for the Rhythm Band

A rhythm band is very versatile. Here are some suggestions and ways you can improvise using materials found in the environment.

Sticks are always easy to make and easy to use. If you have spindles from old used furniture such as cradles or chairs, they make excellent sticks. They can be rubbed together, tapped together or used with a drum. They are usually made of wood and can therefore be painted as well. For young children, painting faces on them or painting them with metallic paint is great fun and makes the sticks look great. Playing with your own decorated sticks is even greater fun.

Drums can be made from the lid of any box. Hat boxes and shoe boxes with lids can be painted and decorated.

Bells are easy to make and make nice sounding instruments. Bells can be purchased in many sizes and shapes. These bells can be strung together with cord or ribbon.

Before using any of these instruments, explain what a beat is. A beat is one strike of a stick or one shake of a bell. It is like the tick of a clock. Explain that a note means sound and a rest means silence.

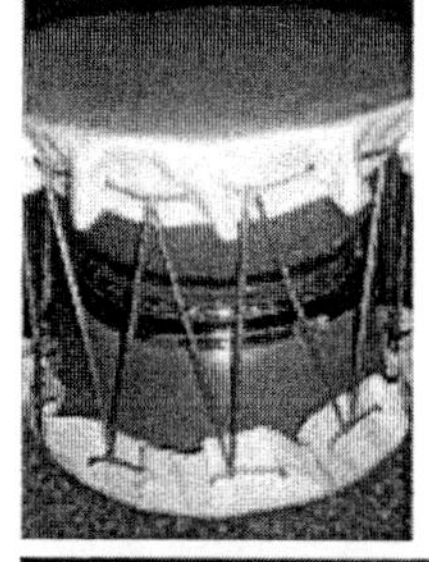

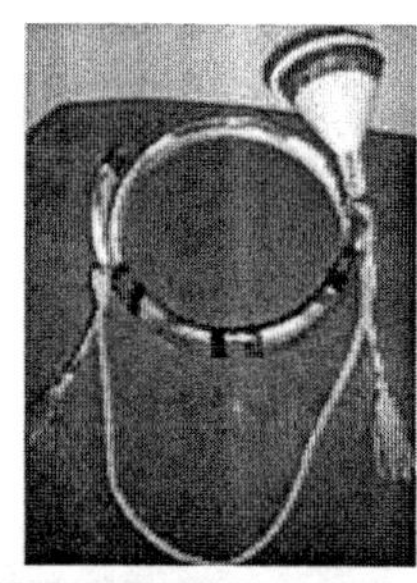

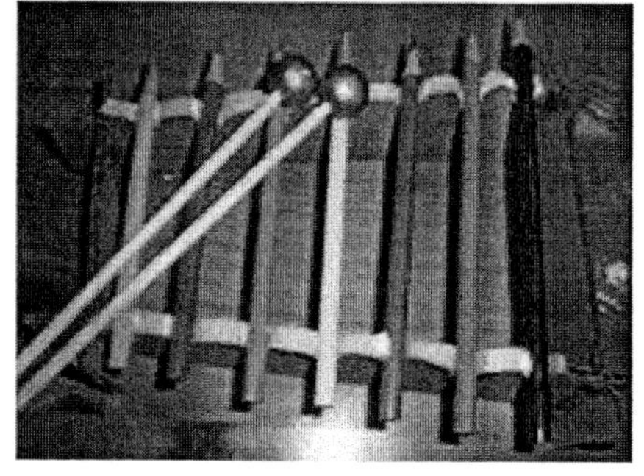

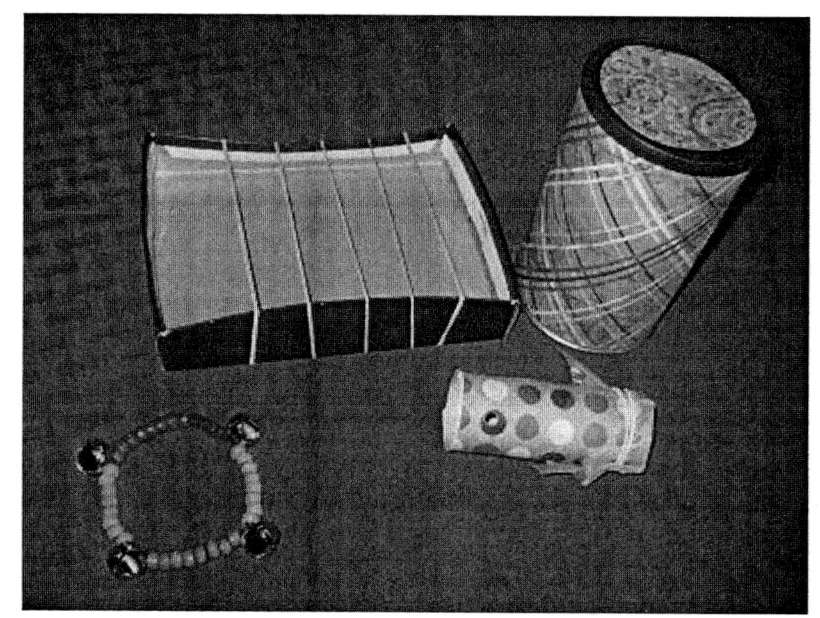

Teacher Notes:

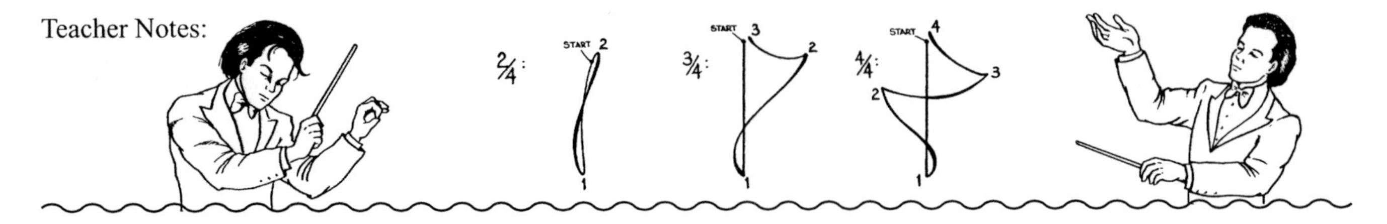


In this section there are worksheets for the Keyboard, Band Instruments, the musical story called "Music School in Musicland," and musical terms such as The Note, The Rest, The Treble Clef, and The Bass Clef.

1. **Keyboard:**
   The keyboard on a piano or organ should be discussed. Students will recognize that the keyboard is made up of black and white keys. There are more white keys than black keys and the black keys are found in groups of two and groups of three. The two worksheets provided on pages 35 and 36 will promote this concept.

2. **Band Instruments:**
   The band and its instruments should be discussed. Try to provide examples of these instruments in picture form and discuss them. The three worksheets on pages 37 to 39 will help students recognize the concept of one beat and that a band uses four beats when they march. Some percussion instruments are introduced as well.

3. **Music School in Musicland:**
   The story on pages 40 to 44 may be reproduced and collated to form a storybook. The story should be discussed and the pictures can be colored by the students. The story introduces other band instruments and the terms composer and conductor. Be sure to explain the difference between these terms.

4. **Notes and Rests:**
   The worksheets on pages 45 to 46 concentrate on the the types of notes and rests found in music. Explain to the students that a musical note is made up of a head and a stem. Draw various notes on the chalkboard or on chart paper.

   Introduce the musical symbol that signifies a rest. Draw the rests on the chalkboard or chart paper. Explain that when you are playing music and you see a rest there is no sound or there is silence.

5. **Treble Clef and Bass Clef:**
   Show pictures of a treble clef and a bass clef to your students. Discuss the shape of each one. Explain that the treble clef is used for high pitched music while the bass clef is used for lower pitched music. The worksheets found on pages 47 to 48 are to be used to strengthen this concept.

6. **Review Sheets:**
   The worksheets on pages 49 to 55 are to be used to review all the concepts taught.

7. **Stencils:**
   This sheet is to be used for tracing the formation of rests. It is to be reproduced, mounted on a sturdy backing, and laminated. The students will trace the shapes and make them into creatures, insects, etc.

Color the words "THE KEYBOARD" and connect the dots.

Draw two big white things.

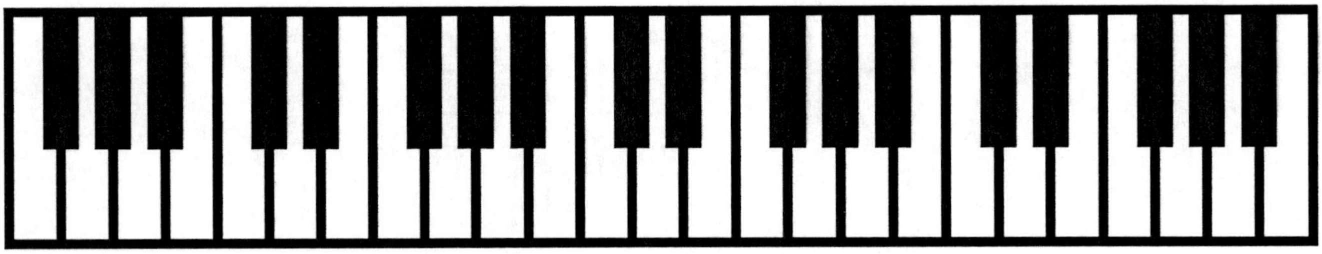

Draw five little black things.

Color her and give her a name. ________________________________

ISBN: 9781554950843

# CYMBOLS GO CRASH! IN A BAND

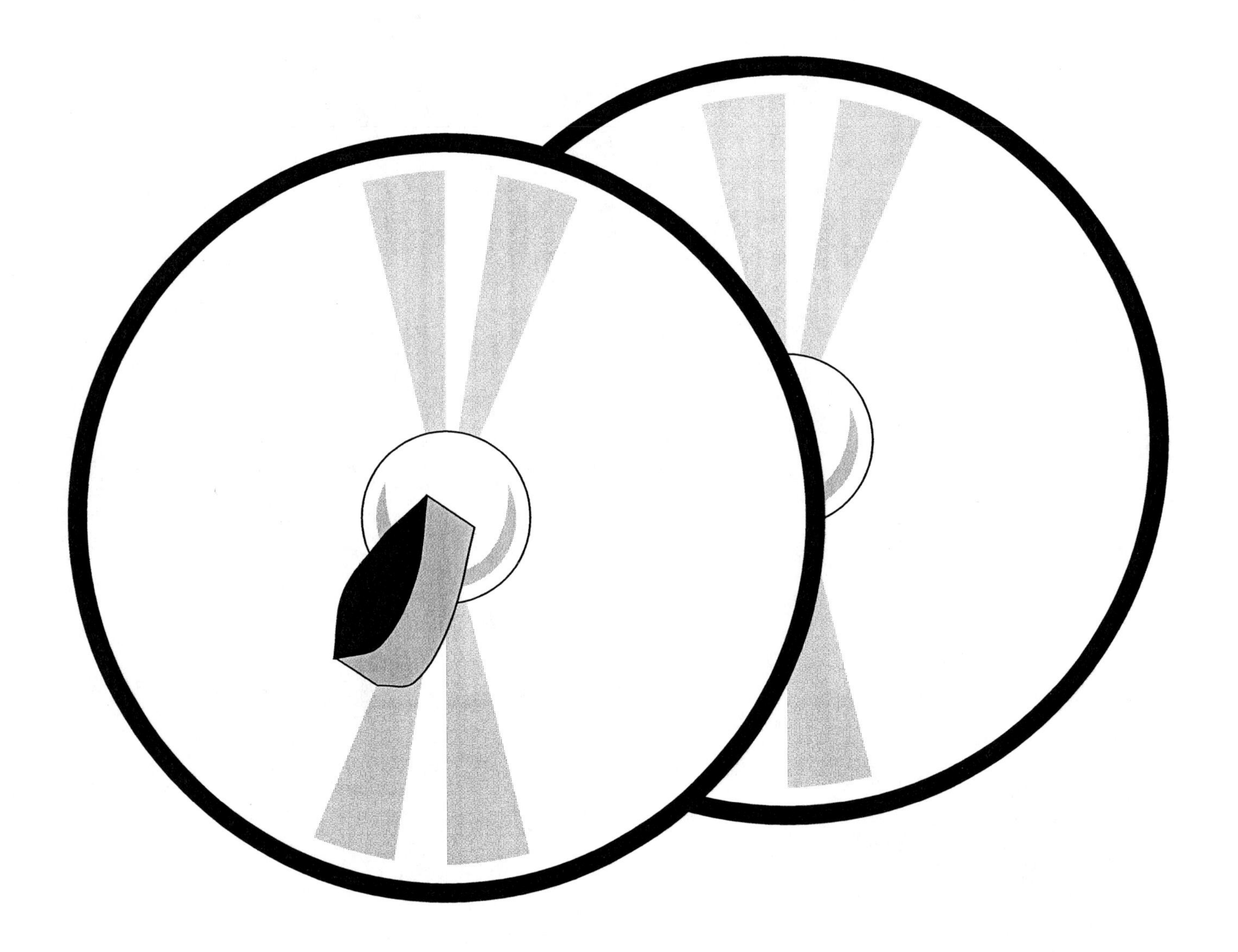

Color the word crash and make some designs on the cymbols.
Make them colorful as a clown is going to use them in his clown band.

Trace this word.

One hit of the drumstick is one beat.

This note ♩ means one beat. Draw one beat notes everywhere.

ISBN: 9781554950843

# MUSIC SCHOOL IN MUSICLAND

Before the instruments learn their lessons they play in the playground.

ISBN: 9781554950843

Today the teacher wants to know what everyone wants to be when they grow up.

Patty Piccolo wants to sing in the opera.

Cindy Castanet wants to be a conductor.
She practises on the baby bells to direct music.

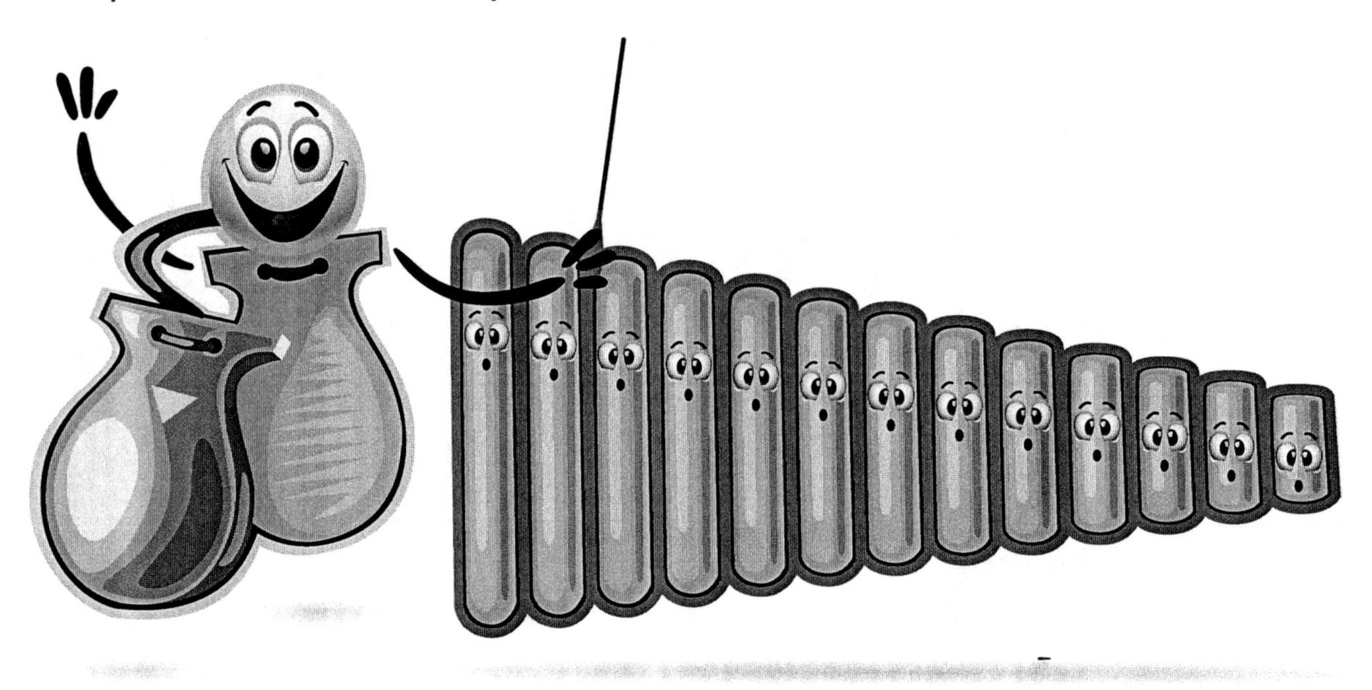

The timpani twins love to write music so they want to be composers.

Tara Trumpet wants to be a teacher.

Help her count.

Tony Tuba likes to exercise upside down.
He wants to be a gym teacher.

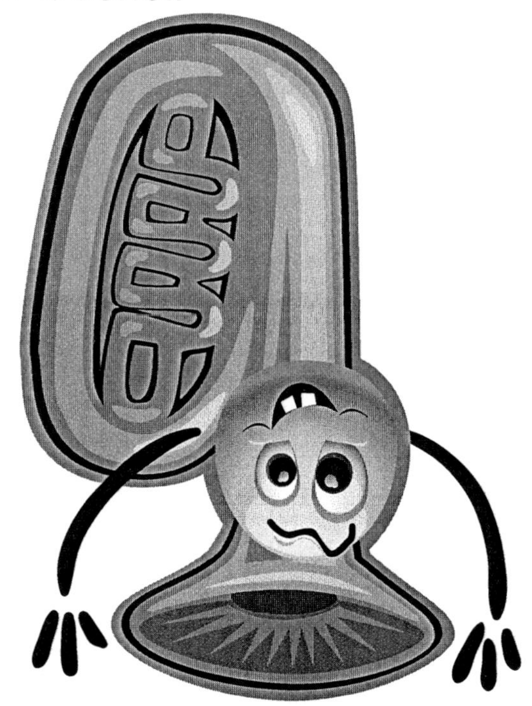

Sassy Saxophone wants to be a farmer.
There will be a lot of music on his farm.

Draw a picture of what you would like to be.

# THE MUSICAL TOP

Connect the dots.

Color all the notes black.

Count the notes. How many? ____

ISBN: 9781554950843

# Notes have a head. 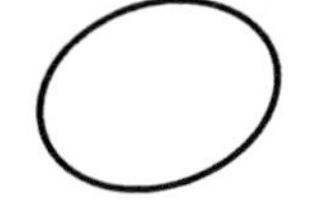

# Some rests look like hats.

This brass instrument is blowing out the notes which make a sound and rests which are silent.

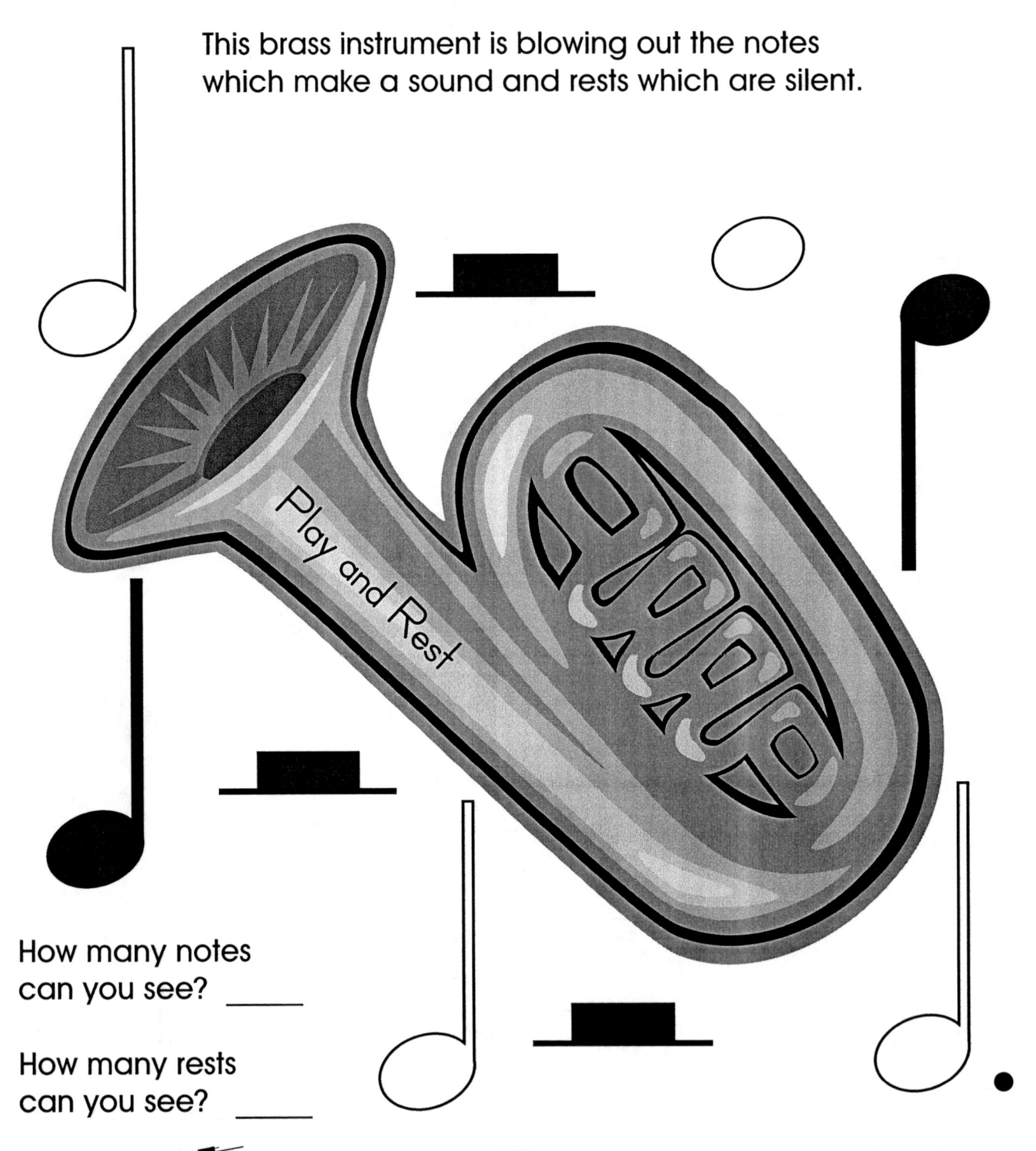


How many notes can you see? _____

How many rests can you see? _____

ISBN: 9781554950843

# SIGNS, SIGNS

Color the crayons four different colors.

Now use each of the four colors to trace the music signs.

Draw signs that you see when you are traveling, walking or riding a bike.

# CLEF COLOR

Color the sections with a treble clef yellow and the sections with a bass clef brown. Finish the picture.

A treble clef is for high notes.

A bass clef is for low notes.

# Match the signs and color the rainbow.

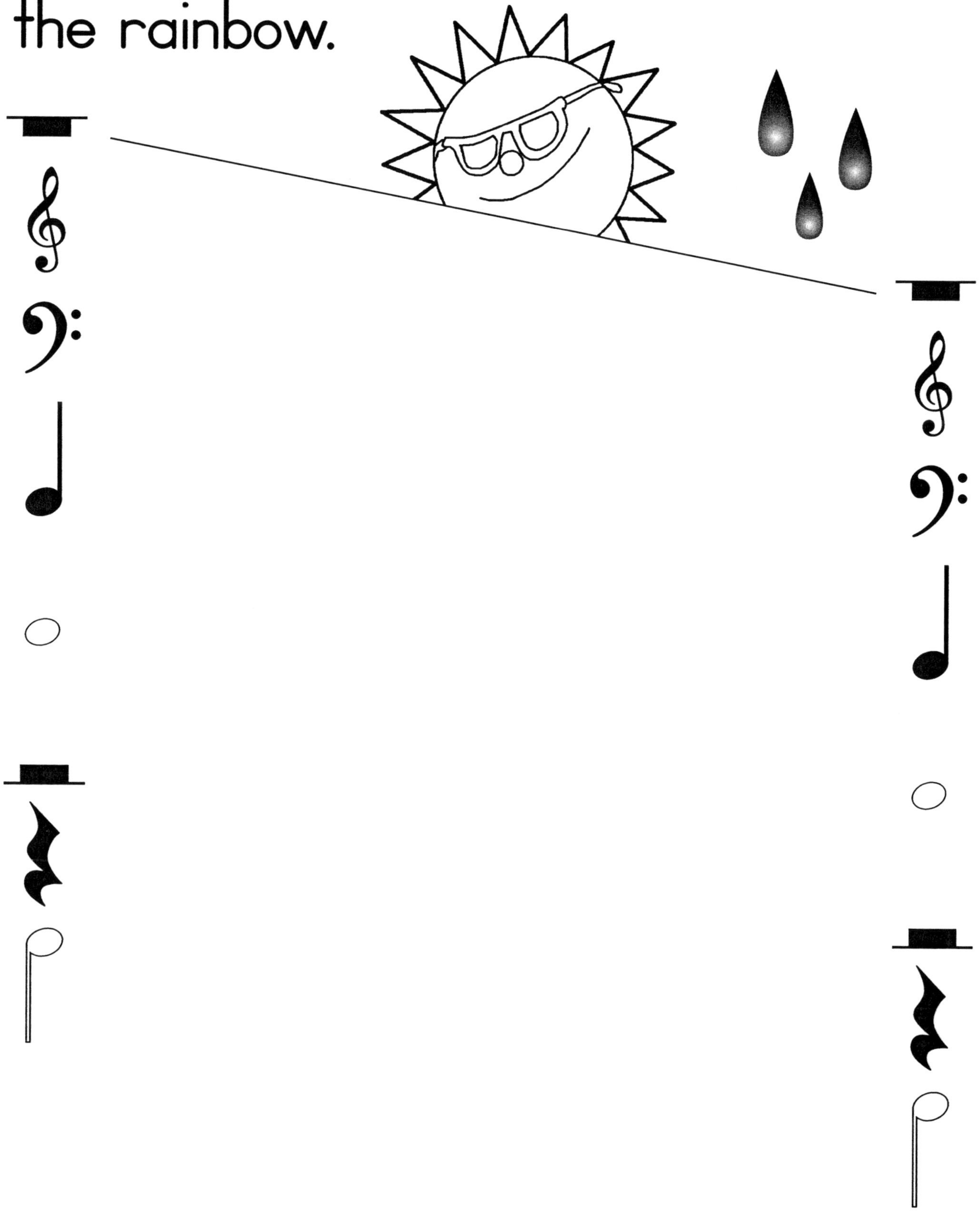

# The Spooky Find

These are notes.
Notes make a sound.

These are rests.
Rests are silent.

Follow the notes so Ghosty Ghost can find his way and get to his home.

ISBN: 9781554950843

# Sweet Music

Treble clefs are used for high notes.

Bass clefs are used for low notes.

Color the spaces in which the treble clefs are red and the spaces in which the bass clefs are green.

# My Music Tree

Decorate the tree with notes. Draw some gifts under the tree.

# Let It Snow

Connect the dots to see what this rest is shaped like.

Draw a face and buttons on the snowman.

# Bass to Bass

How many bass clefs can you find? Circle them.

How many did you find? ______ Draw some more bass clefs.

ISBN: 9781554950843

# SPRING DESIGN

Connect the dots on the Easter Eggs to complete the music signs.

Finish decorating the eggs.

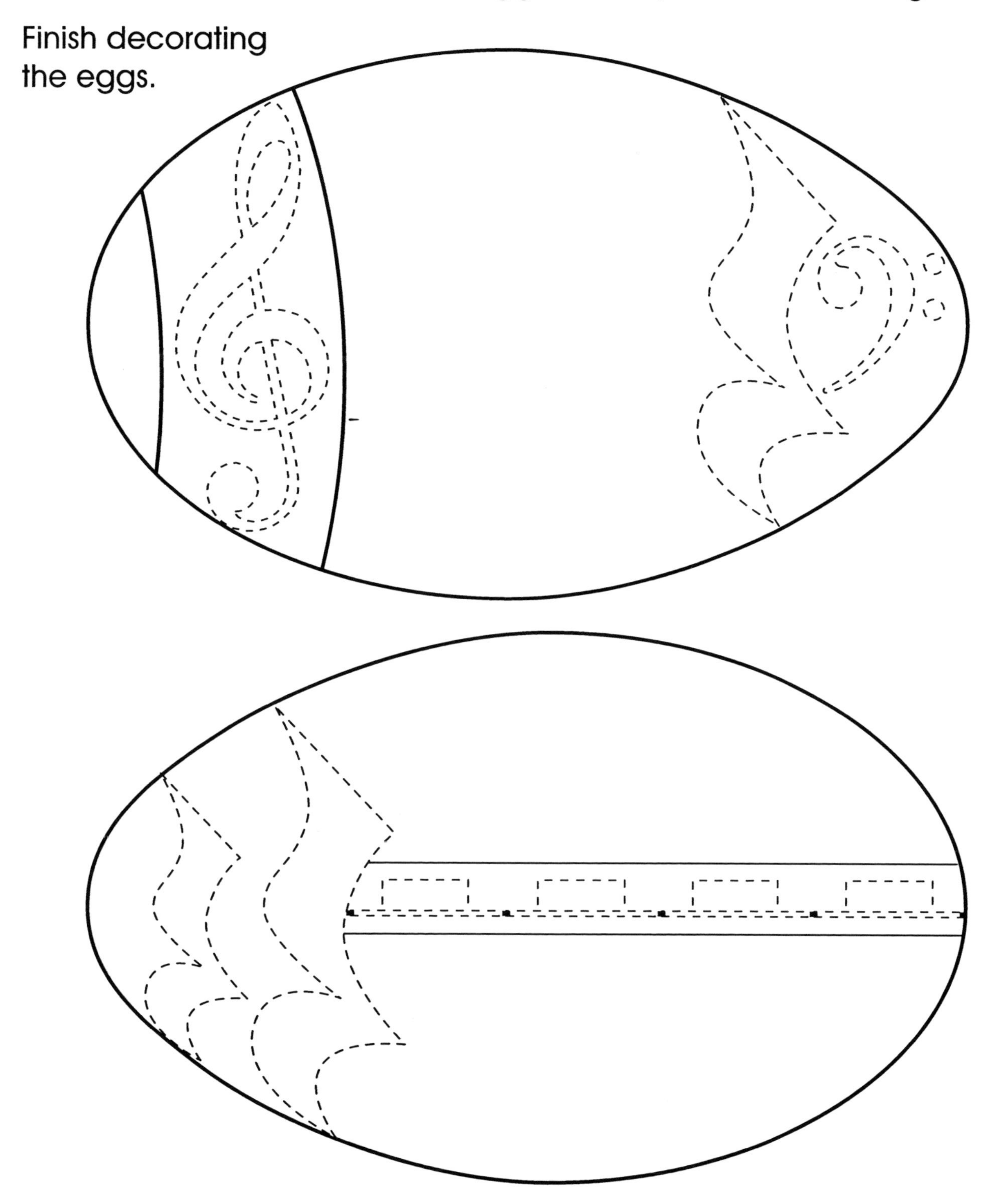

# STENCILS

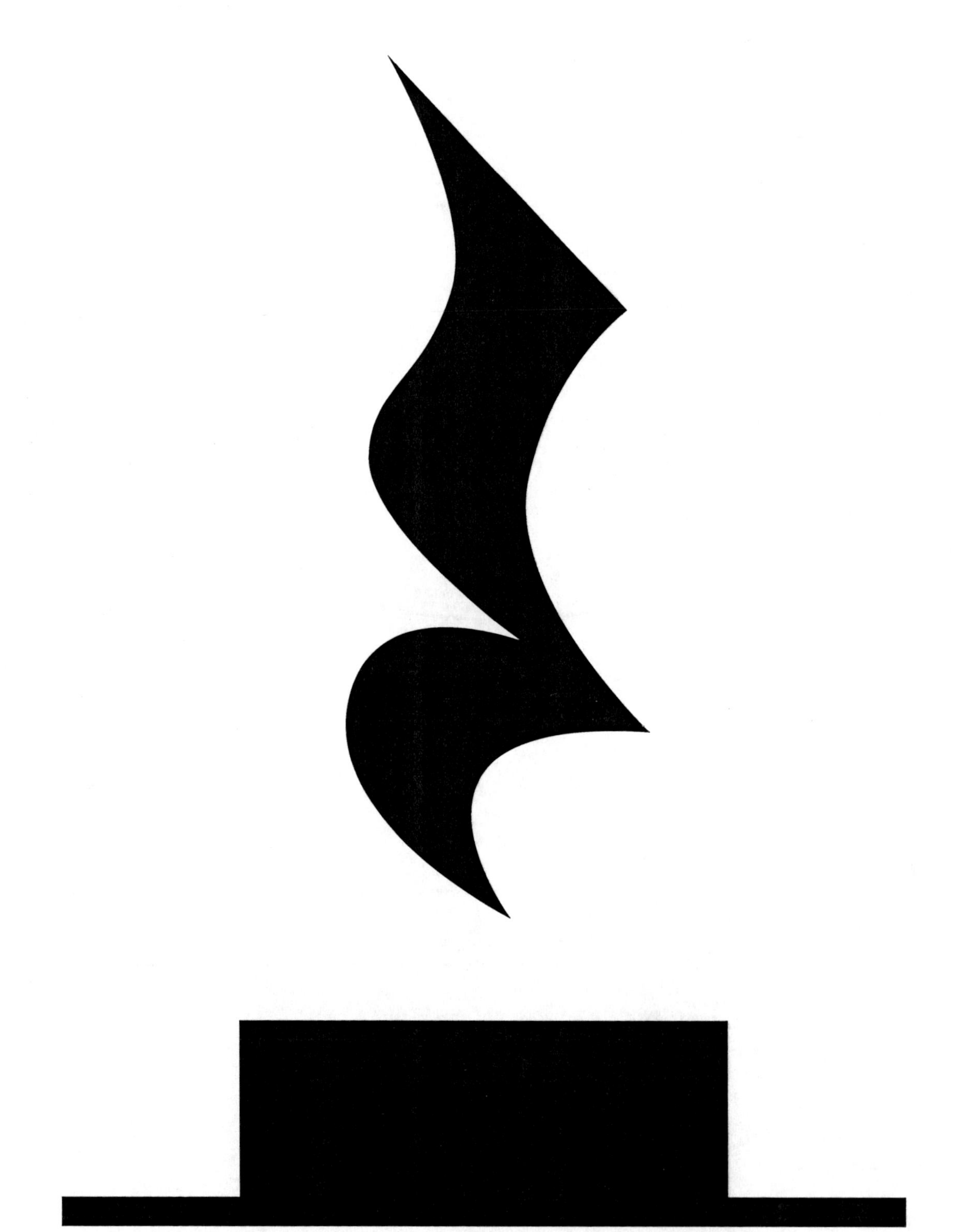

Teacher Notes:

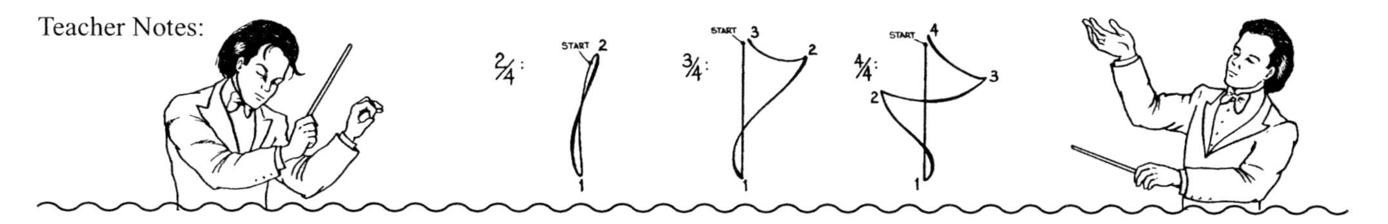


# Developing Music Skills in Grade 1

**Introduction:**

The activities in this section have three intentions:

- to encourage students to be creative.
- to encourage their enjoyment of music.
- to educate them in the field of music.

Since creativity is very important in music, there will be various ways that the work will be completed. The students should enjoy this program and take a positive approach to music. They may like to take the information home or to other environments. Music is everywhere and is a universal language. The students might be amazed at the effect it has on people's lives and the endless variety of music that exists.

The concepts introduced are the percussion instruments, the one beat note, the one beat rest, the staff, the treble clef, pitch, A B C D E F G, the musical alphabet, singing do to do and the composer Chopin.

**Implementing the Ideas into a Music Program:**

1. Each exercise will have a main point or idea, a sign to learn or a musical activity to finish.

2. If there are small dots, the student is to connect the dots to help them form letters, signs or directions.

3. A variety of materials are encouraged such as crayons, markers, colored paper or other available supplies.

4. The students could make a musical booklet to keep their work altogether and this could be used for reference.

5. When their booklet or amount of knowledge and activities are complete, the students can receive a certificate with or without testing, depending on the teacher.

6. The games will reinforce the knowledge learned.

7. A prize board is a great incentive but is optional.

8. The concepts introduced are the percussion instruments, the one beat note and the rest, the staff, the treble clef, pitch, A B C D E F G, the musical alphabet, singing do to do, and the composer Chopin.

Teacher Notes:

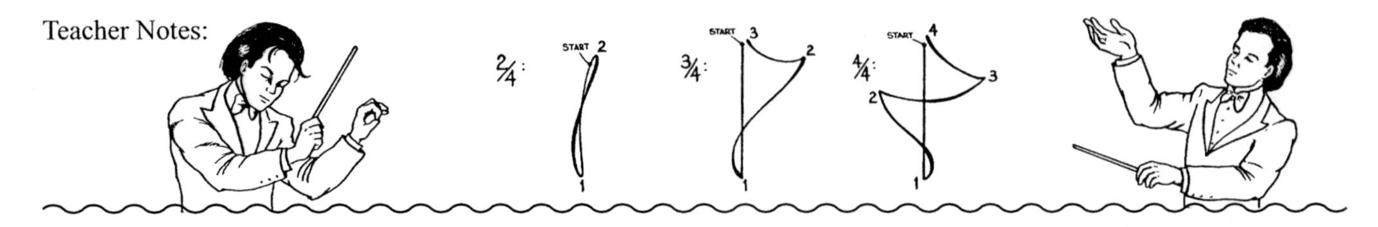

# List of Materials

- Worksheets will be done with a variety of coloring materials.

- Crayons of different textures and colors, markers or pencil crayons of different shades are very effective.

- Graphite pencils will be needed for drawing.

- For the shakers you will need two paper plates or a toilet paper roll, tissue paper, staples, dried beans, paint, and other material you can glue onto paper plates or tubes, glue, a stapler, and scissors.

- For the games you will need construction paper, glue, a score page, a foil paper plate, a duotang, and an arrow made of plastic.

- Tapping sticks or other tapping instruments could be used for the songs to sing in the classroom.

- The best materials for the stencils are crayons of some sort. If the reproducibles are being used under a paper, regular crayons are great to shade on the top sheet to make designs, but if the reproducibles are being traced by the student, they will need pencil crayons or a pencil and regular crayons to color. The reproducibles need to be backed onto cardboard and cut out to give them some thickness. They wear out so extra copies should be made.

- Incentives, such as prizes for a prize board, are great for encouragement. The prize board would have to be prepared with construction paper and coloring material. Prizes could include music stickers, erasers or small items.

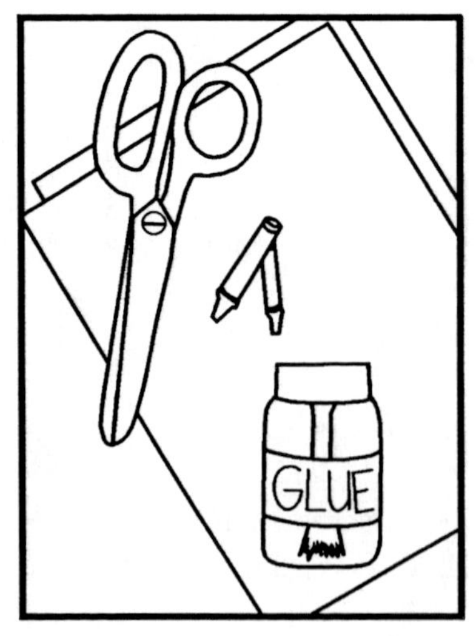

Teacher Notes:

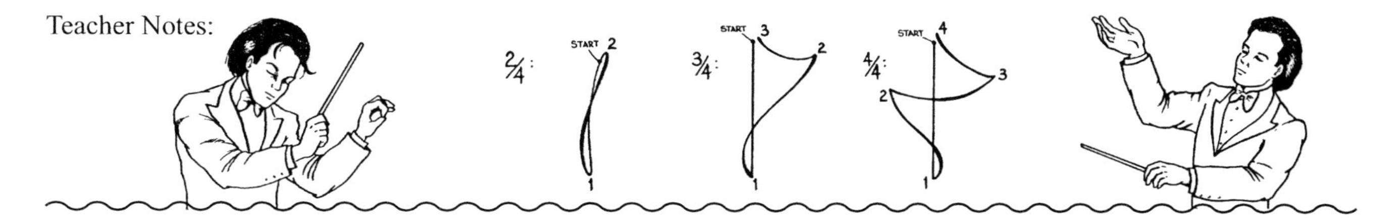


# Teaching Suggestions

- Display signs or musical characters in the classroom.
- Be familiar with the music terms at this level.
- Try having the children work individually, in groups, and/or as a class.
- If working in groups, rotate them at different work stations.
- Different textured crayons work great and go a long way while completing the worksheets.
- Make the shakers before doing the songs in the classroom.
- Students with some knowledge of music should be grouped with students who do not have any knowledge of music.
- Assemble games and boards ahead of time.
- Encourage the students to think of music at home and in other environments.
- Encourage creativity and enjoyment at all times.
- If possible, bring instruments into the classroom.

Teacher Notes:

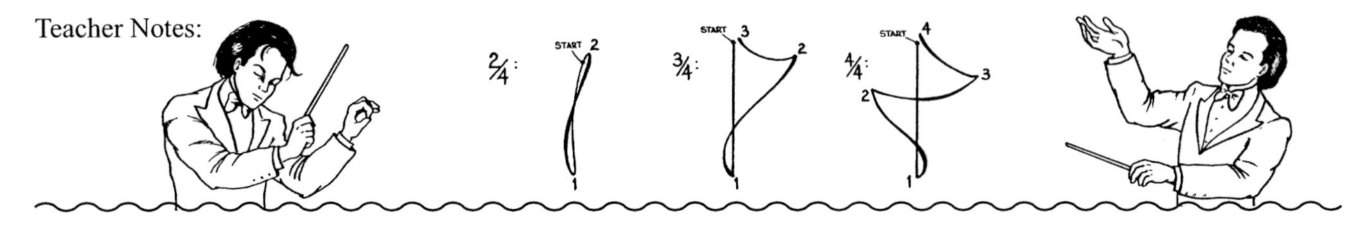


# Music Glossary

**Percussion Instruments:** Percussion instruments are struck, hit or shaken. In this book they include the timpani drums, the triangle, the cymbals, the bells, the keyboard, the maracas, and the tambourine.

**Notes:** When you see a note, there needs to be a sound made by an instrument or voice.

**Rests:** Rests are periods of silence.

**One Beat:** One beat is one count, like the tick of a clock. Tick, tock would therefore be two beats or two counts. When resting for one beat, there needs to be a period of silence for the count of one. Imagine a clock ticking. When explaining this to children, it is easier to put in the word rest when there is silence. So tick, tock, tick, [rest], tick, tock tick, [rest]. [Put in the musical symbol for rest when it says the word [rest] This would be tick, tock, tick, rest (silence); tick, tock, tick, rest, (silence). The exercise with the sticks will help this concept.

**High and Low Pitch:** Some instruments play in a higher range or pitch just like some voices have a higher range or pitch. The high range uses the treble clef and the lower range uses other clefs learned at a later time.

**Treble Clef:** The treble clef is used for the highest pitched instruments or the higher end of keyboard instruments. The middle point of the treble clef centers all around the G line of the staff and sometimes can be called the G clef.

**Staff:** The five lines and four spaces that music is written on is called a staff. Sometimes more than one staff is connected and they will be called staves.

**Composer:** A composer is a song-writer from the past or present.

Teacher Notes:

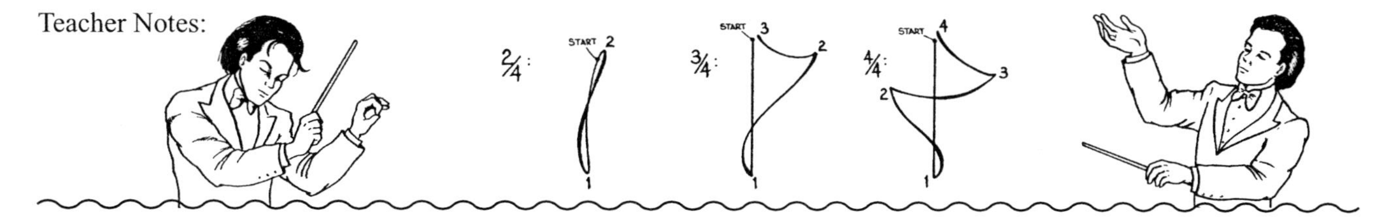

# Percussion Instruments

- The story of the percussion instrument characters will introduce the students to the instruments. This may be made into a storybook for each student to color and read or may be part of their music booklet.

- The teacher may also have some percussion instruments to demonstrate to the class or students may have some of these instruments at home.

- The worksheets, that follow, will help the student remember what has been learned. Shapes, numbers, and the alphabet are also included along with the characters.

- The organization of groups, music booklets, and the prize board should all be completed prior to the beginning of this topic.

- The shakers will add enjoyment to this part of the book and can be used with the songs.

- Creativity and enjoyment are the most important keys in music advancement.

# THE NOISY DAY AT THE MARACAS

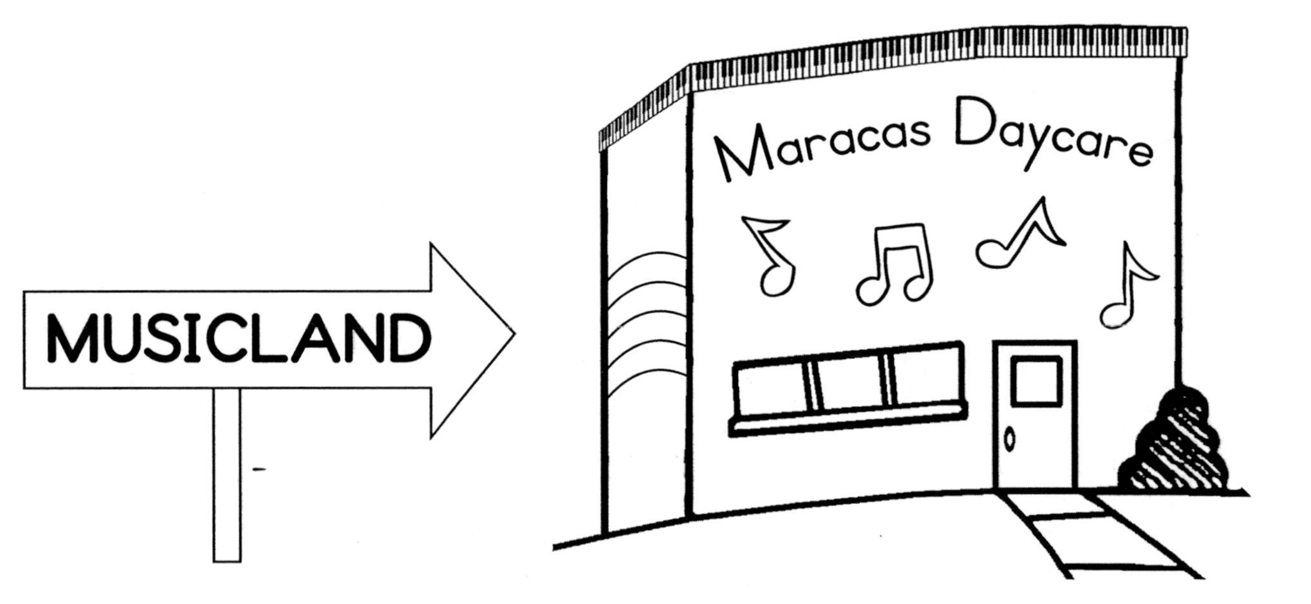


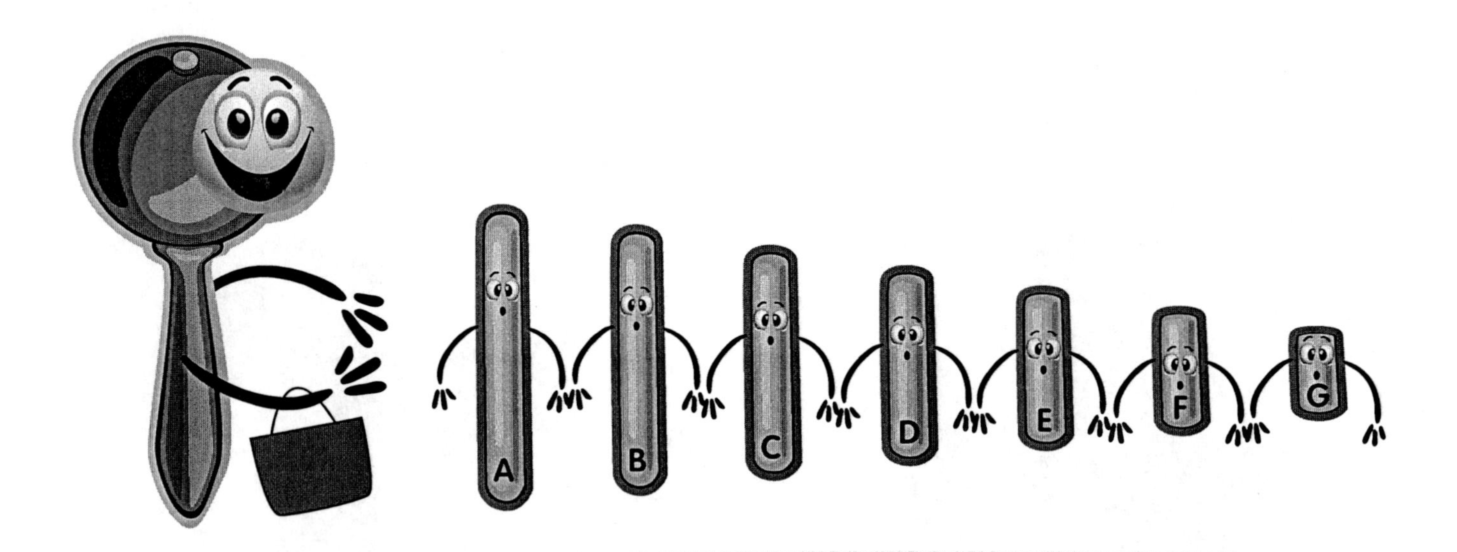


The Maracas family ran the town daycare in MusicLand. Mrs. Maracas put the seven baby bells down for a nap. They had soft tiny voices. Their names were A, B, C, D, E, F, and G Bell. They sang themselves to sleep.

The Cymbal twins were busy banging their heads together.
This made a loud crash but because it was nap time they had to stop.

The timpani twins were in the backyard tapping their heads with a drumstick. They were very noisy and got the dog barking so they stopped and also went in for their nap.

Tara Triangle was so soft and sweet that she almost got left behind. Tammy Tambourine, whose bells would shake and ring whenever she walked, took Tara by the hand. They also went inside.

After their nap, all the instruments had a concert together because they were all rested up. The bells sang do, re, me, fa, sol, la, ti, do. The others counted 1, 2, 3, 4, 1, 2, 3, 4 and tapped or shook to the beat. Then all the parents came and took the instruments home and the Maracas family rested, in silence.

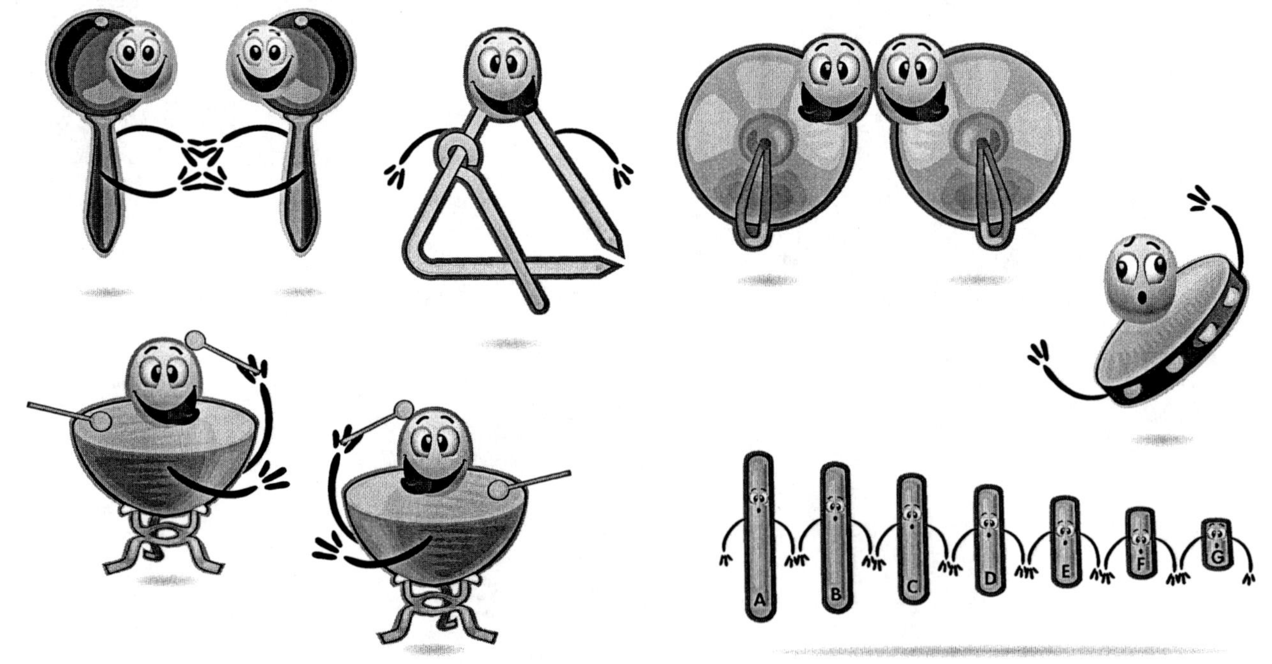


ISBN: 9781554950843

# Is It Tapped or Shaken?

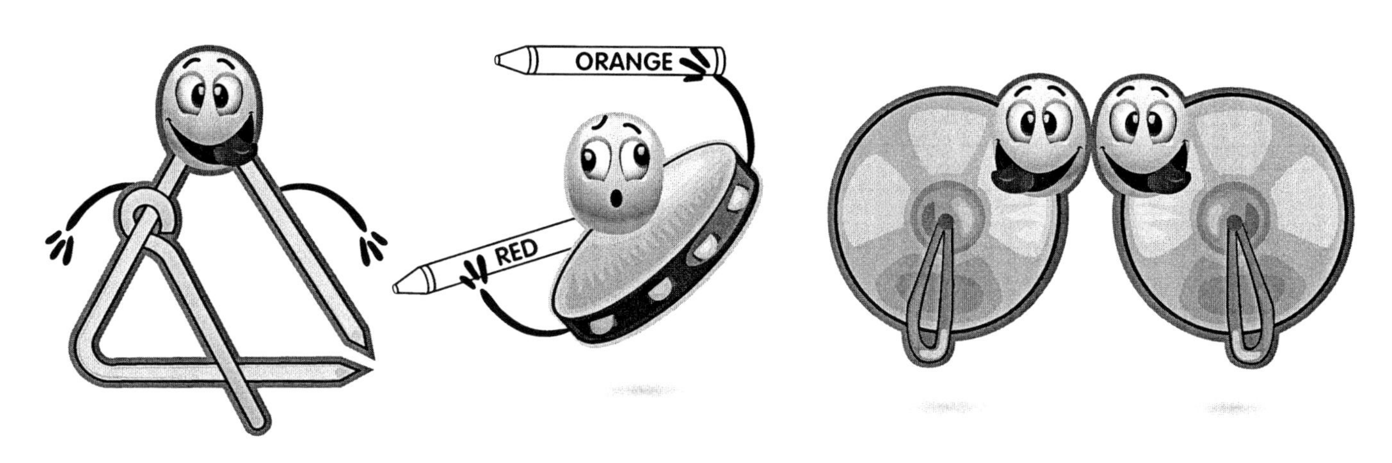


Some percussion instruments are hit or struck while others are shaken. Tammy Tambourine can be tapped or shaken.

She needs help circling in red all the instruments that are tapped for a sound and in orange all the instruments that are shaken for a sound.

# Bedtime for Baby Bells

Tommy Timpani is learning about rectangles. Help him put the baby Bells in their beds.

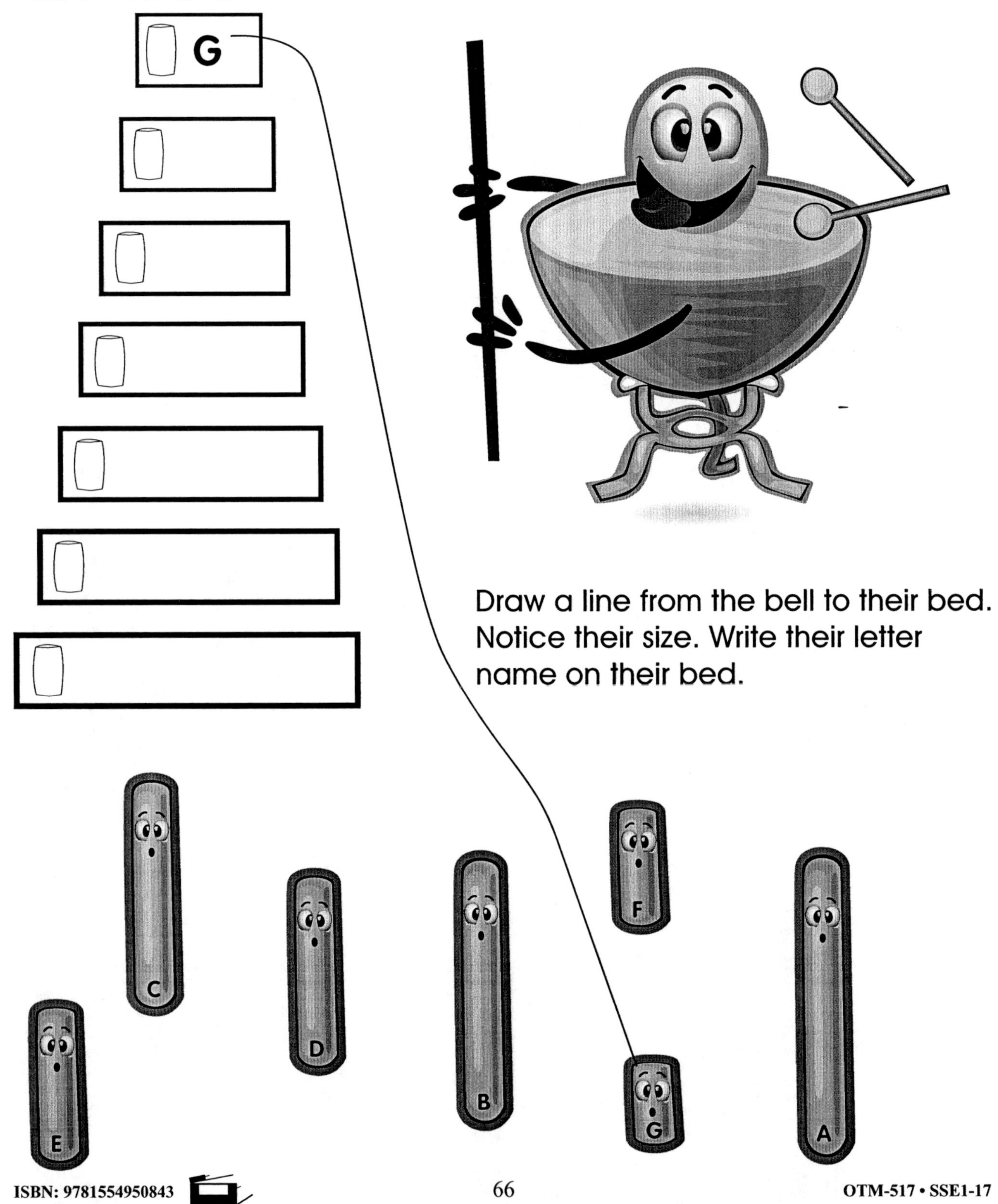


Draw a line from the bell to their bed. Notice their size. Write their letter name on their bed.

ISBN: 9781554950843

# What are We?

Connect the 7 letters used in music and the numbers to find out what musical instrument is below.

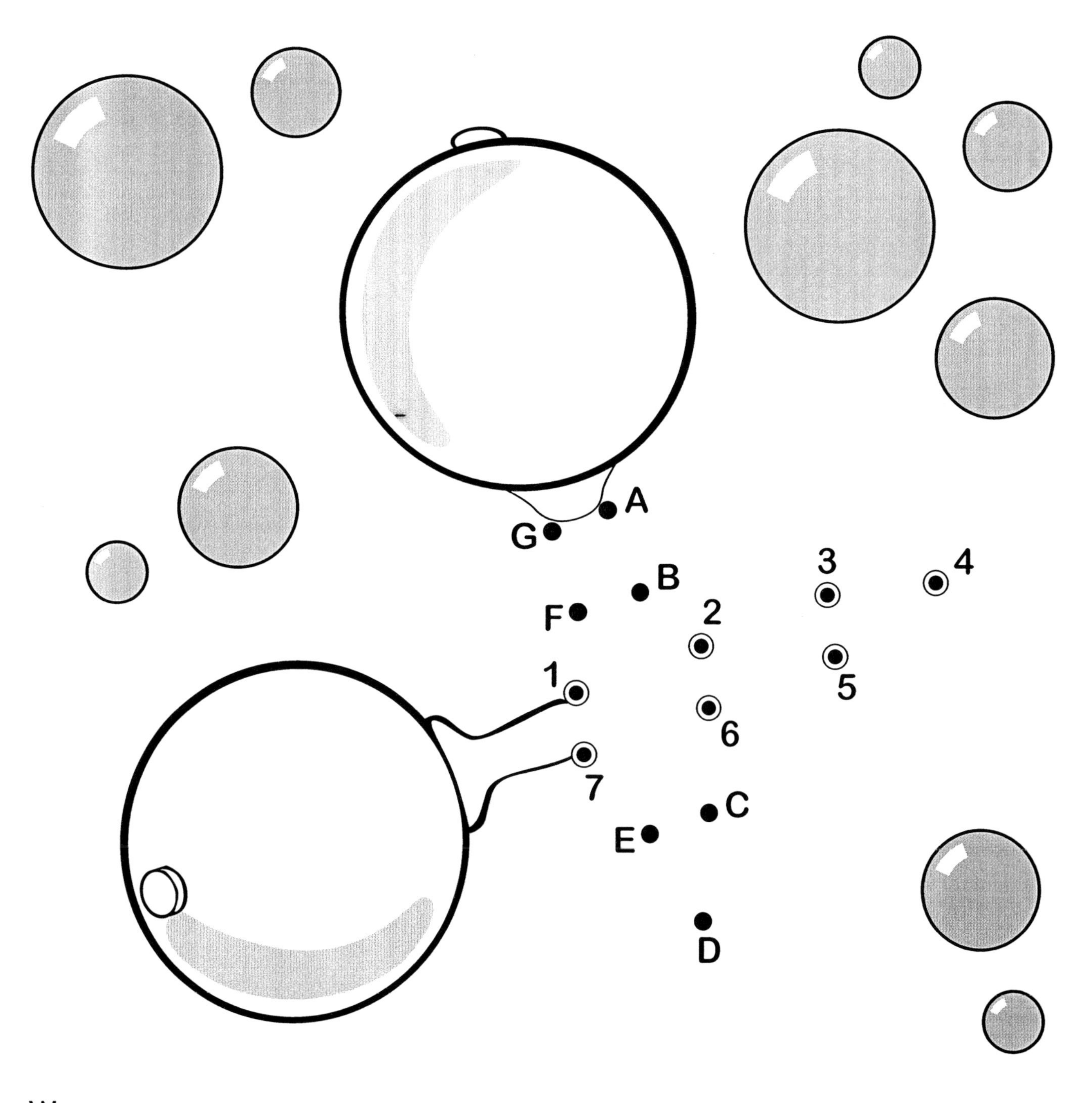


We are ____________________ .

What is around the instrument? ____________________

ISBN: 9781554950843

# Triangles and Circles for Tara and Tammy

Help Tara Triangle and Tammy Tambourine count the triangles and circles in the playground. Draw more triangles and circles.

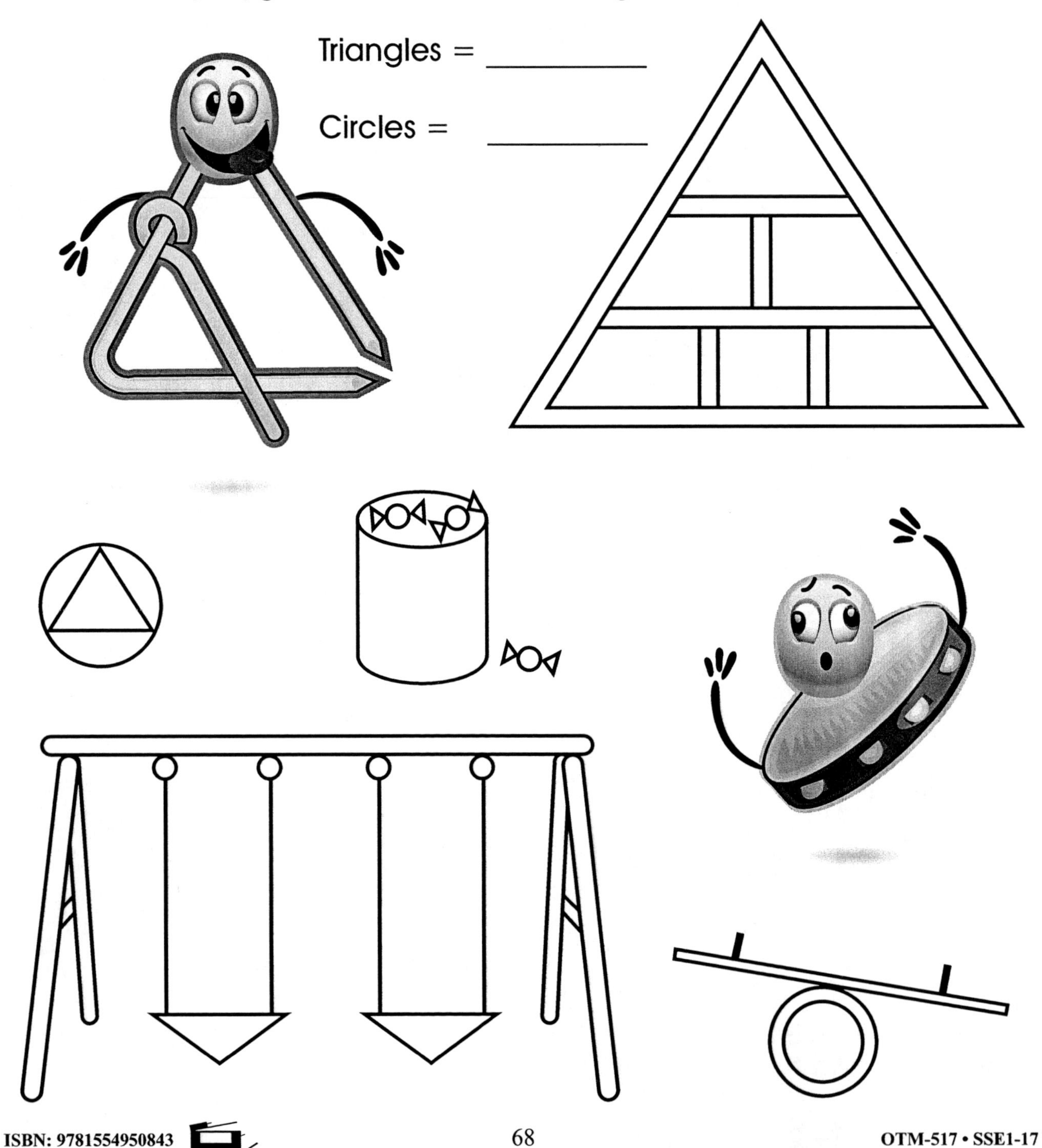

# Answer Sheet

**Tapped or Shaken?** ***(Page 65)***

Tapped instruments include Tara Triangle, The Timpani Twins, The Cymbal Twins (with each other), and The Baby Bells. These should be circled in red.

Shaken instruments include the Maracas Family which should be circled in orange.

**Bedtime for Baby Bells** ***(Page 66)***

Order of the Letters on the beds: G, F, E, D, C, B, A

**Dot to Dot, What are We** ***(Page 67)***

Maracas and bubbles

**Triangles and Circles for Tara and Tammy** ***(Page 68)***

There are 19 triangles and 10 circles.

# Make to Shake

### Teacher Instructions for Shakers

**List of Material Needed:**

| | | | | |
|---|---|---|---|---|
| • paper plates | • toilet paper rolls | • stapler | • scissors | • beans |
| • dried peas | • tissue paper | • glue | • decorations | • beads |

**Instructions:**

1. Each student needs two paper plates or one toilet paper roll.
2. If using toilet paper rolls, you will also need tissue paper for the ends of the rolls. These should be precut into pieces large enough to be doubled up and stapled over the ends of the rolls to hold the beans in.
3. The students should design their shakers using plates or rolls.
4. The paper plates or rolls should be partially stapled together and filled with dried peas or beans. Certain beads will also work.
5. The shakers should be entirely closed so the beans will not fall out.
6. Make the shakers before singing the songs.

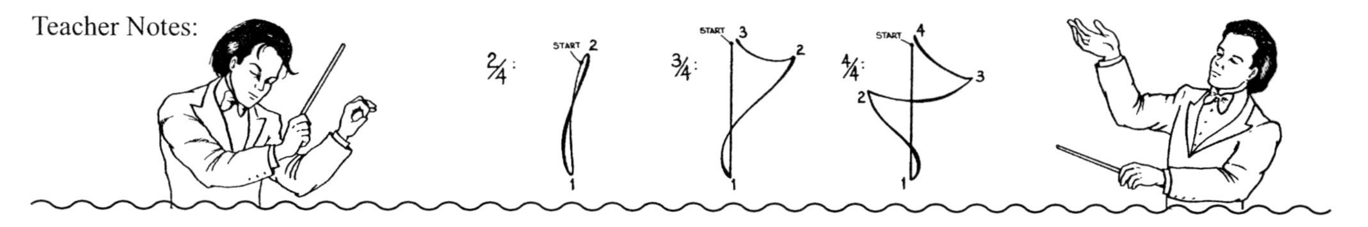


# One Beat

- The display sheet on the one beat note and rest may be displayed in the classroom or copied and added to the students' music booklets. It is found on page 72.

- The exercise on the one beat note on page 73 should be done after explaining what one beat is. See the definition of one beat on page 72. The broken lines help the students to form the notes and the letters. Make sure the notes are colored in, otherwise they get more than one beat.

- The worksheet on the one beat rest on page 74 is also dotted because this is a difficult rest to form. Explain what a rest is before this worksheet is done. Encourage the student to be creative with the worksheets. The worksheet on the fish is a combination of rests and notes.

- The exercises on the notes and rests demonstrate what a note is compared to a rest. The teacher may need to tap this out for the student a number of times before they understand the concept. Once this is learned, the student can also do the exercise with their shakers. The shakers are a little more difficult to control than sticks but this makes it a good test. There shouldn't be a sound during these rests.

- The reproducibles should be cut out and glued onto cardboard at this point. The teacher may want to make many copies of the reproducibles as they wear out quickly. Using the reproducibles can be fun and creative for the students. It is such a flexible exercise since it can be done individually or in groups. Suggestions for the reproducibles are to make insects, other garden creatures or garden flowers. They will spark the imagination of the students. Cards can also be made for special occasions. If some of the younger students cannot trace the reproducibles, they can be placed under the paper and colored over with different colors of crayons such as sparkle crayons.

- It is suggested that the teacher get used to the rhythm of Jo-Jum's Drum Song before using it with the class. If the notes are not known, any monotone note will work with this song. This means you can stay on the same note all the way through and concentrate more on the rhythm. If doing the second verse, make sure you substitute "tap" for "play" and "feet" for "hands."

# The One Beat Note

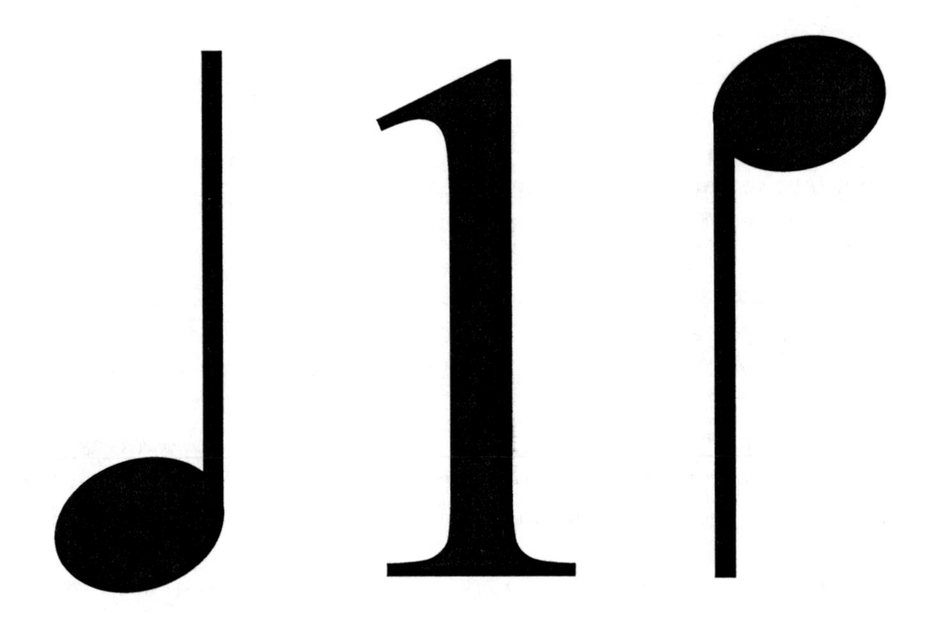


# The One Beat Rest

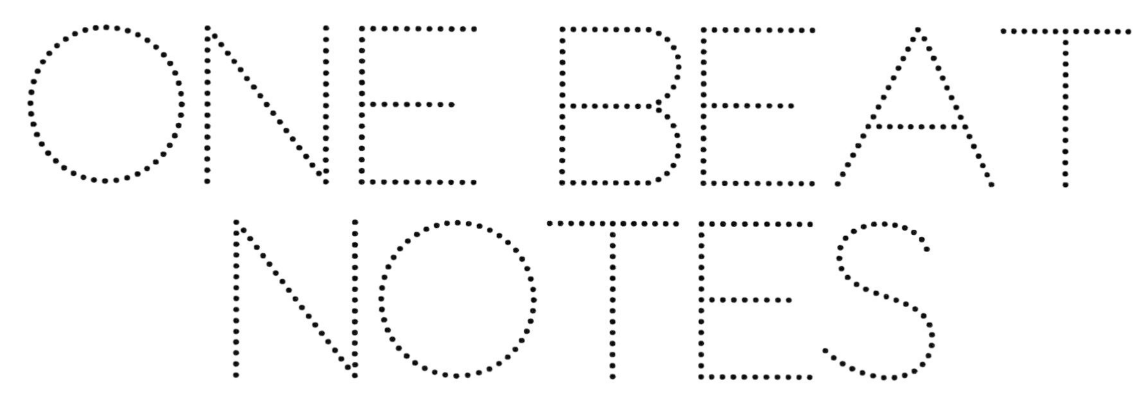


Trace the title and the notes around the drum. Draw some more one beat notes around the drum.
Color them black.

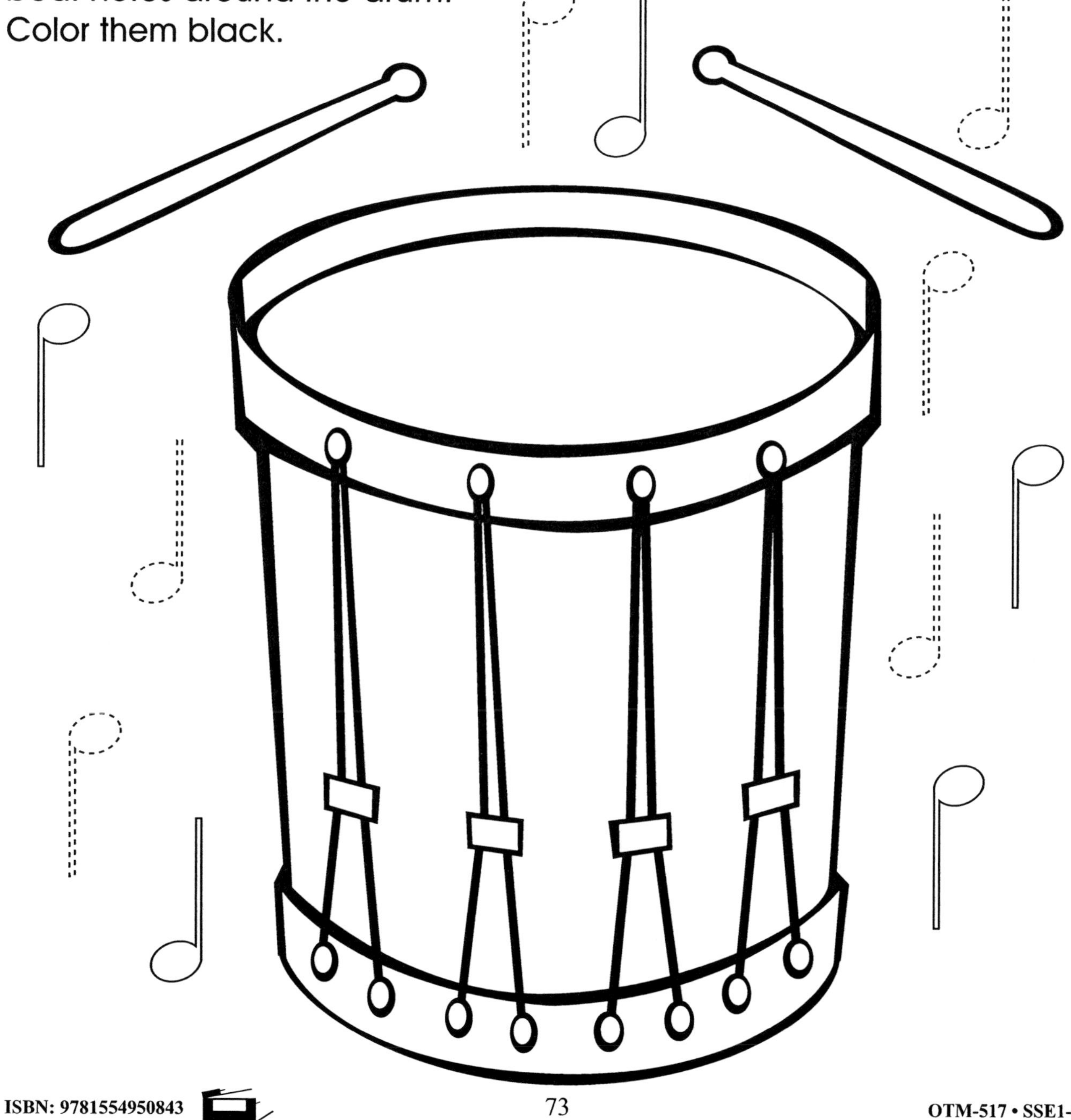

# One Beat Rests

Join the dots on the computer screen to find the one beat rests, make some buttons on the computer.

How many one beat rests did you find?

I found ______ one beat rests.

# One Beat Notes and Rests

Color the fish that have a one beat note yellow.

Color the fish that have a one beat rest orange.

ISBN: 9781554950843

# Tap and Rest

T = Tap  R = Rest

Group 1 and 2:

Each group should be practising this indiviually.

Group 1:

Group 1 should practise this alone.

Group 2:

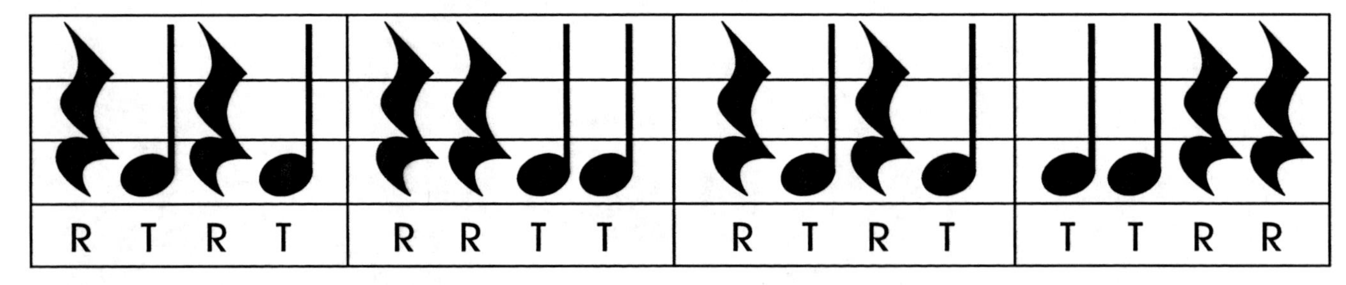


Group 2 should practise this and then they can be played together.

# STENCILS

# Timing for Jo-Jum's Drum

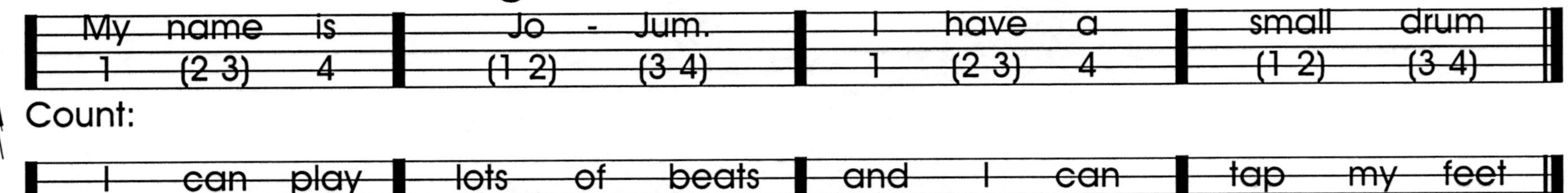


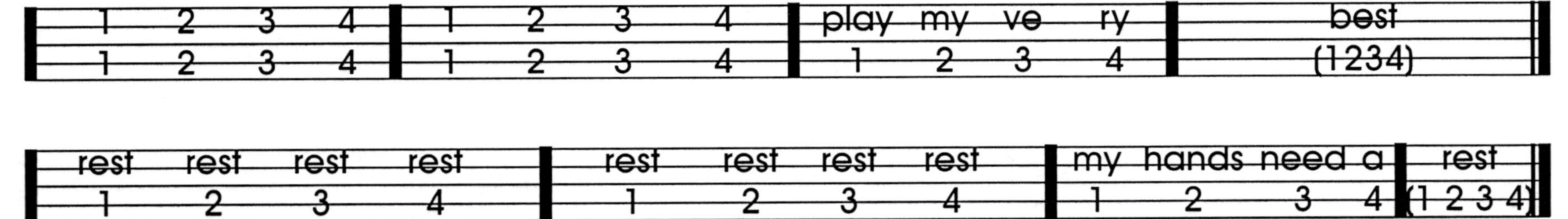


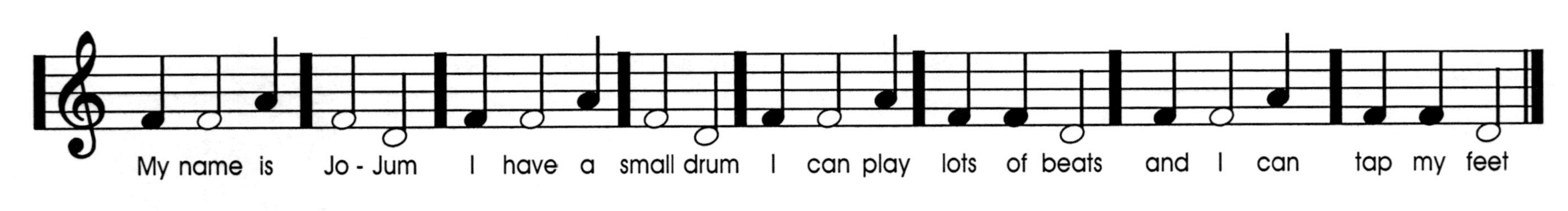


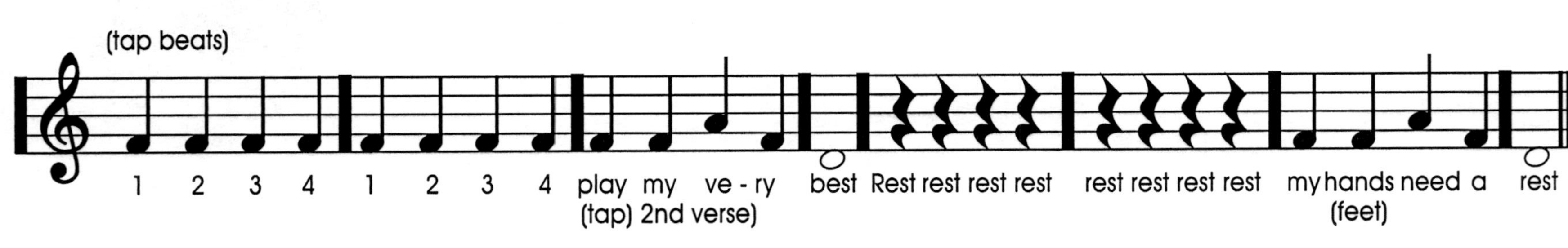


ISBN: 9781554950843

Teacher Notes:

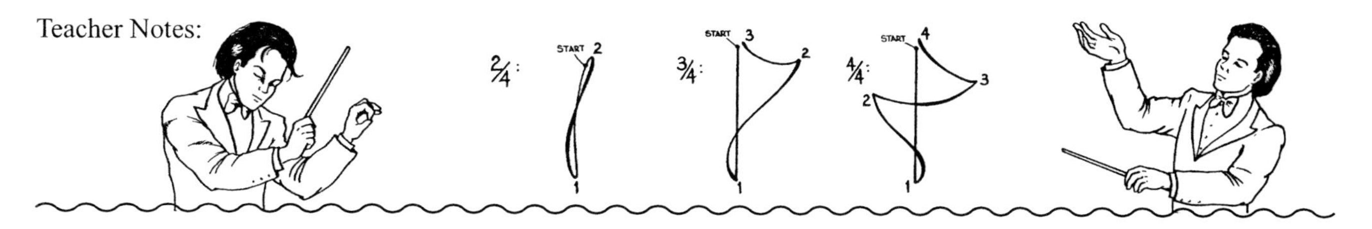


# The Treble Clef, Staff, Letters and Notes Used in Music, Pitch, and the Composer Chopin

- There is a display sheet for the treble clef for the classroom or the students' booklets. The treble clef is used for the instruments with a high pitch. It would be useful to discuss, at this time, the difference in the pitch of instruments or people's voices.

- It is very difficult to draw a treble clef and therefore the dot to dot will help this formation.

- The display sheet on the staff indicates the five lines and four spaces. When counting lines and spaces on a staff, one is always on the bottom because later on, when the students learn the notes, they are figured out from the bottom of the staff.

- The ball exercise is to get the student used to drawing notes in the spaces. It should be pointed out that notes are made with circles.

- The song S T A F F is to get the students used to seeing the treble clef on the staff and to note the spelling. The timing for this song is as follows:

| | | | | | | | | | | | |
|---|---|---|---|---|---|---|---|---|---|---|---|
| | S | T | A | F | F | look | at | the | dou | ble | F |
| Count: | 123 | 123 | 12 | 3 | 123 | 1 | 2 | 3 | 12 | 3 | 123 |
| | S | T | A | F | F | Now | with | a | tre | ble | clef |
| | 123 | 123 | 123 | 123 | 123 | 1 | 2 | 3 | 12 | 3 | 123 |

- If you do not know how to sing the do (pronounced like dough) to do scale with the class and you have a small keyboard or piano, go to the white key directly before the group of two black keys. This is C, in piano, which will be do. The next white key up will be D or re, and so on, until you reach the next C, or high do. Therefore, you would play 8 white keys in a row for do, re, mi, fa, sol, la, ti, do. You'll notice underneath the STAFF song the letters are written to sing this with do, re, me, fa, sol, la, ti, do.

Teacher Notes:

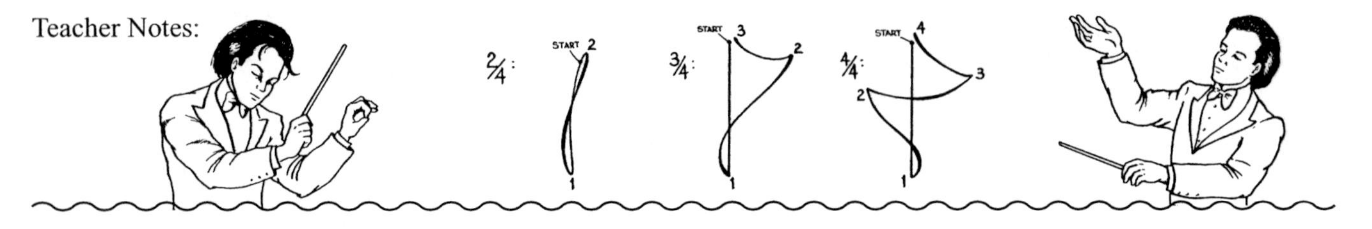


# The Treble Clef, Staff, Letters and Notes Used in Music, Pitch and the Composer Chopin

- When singing the Do to Do Song, sing the whole first line on the C Key. Then sing the whole second line on the D key.

- Sing the whole third line on the E key and so on until you end up singing the last line on high C. This makes the song simple and shows how the pitch gets one note higher each line.

- The exercise matching the balloons on the stairs indicates the rise in the tones, showing that they get higher in pitch.

- The other worksheets are to familiarize the student with the musical alphabet, the seven letters used in music.

- The composer, Chopin, is also introduced in this unit. Learning history can be boring, but if the students can relate the facts to themselves, it becomes more interesting. The student should answer questions about themsleves and the facts about the composer will stick in their minds easier.

- The teacher is able to reproduce a book for each student to color and answer questions.

- For added knowledge and to familiarize the student with Chopin, some of his music could be played in the classroom. "Nocturne in E Flat" is found on some lullaby tapes. Also two lighter tunes are "The Minute Waltz" written for a dog, and the "Cat Waltz," inspired by Chopin's cat jumping on the piano.

# The Treble Clef

# What's My Name?

What musical sign does this make?

Trace the dots from A to Z carefully.

Hint: A __ reble ___ lef

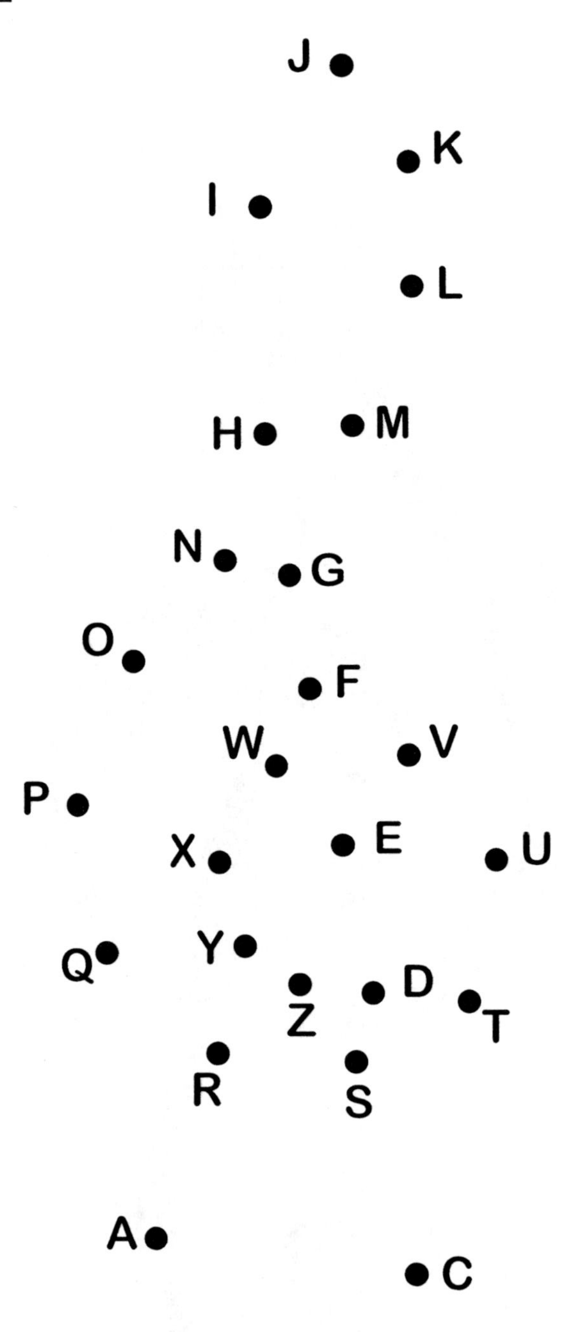

# The Staff

Music is written on a staff.

A staff is made of five lines and four spaces.

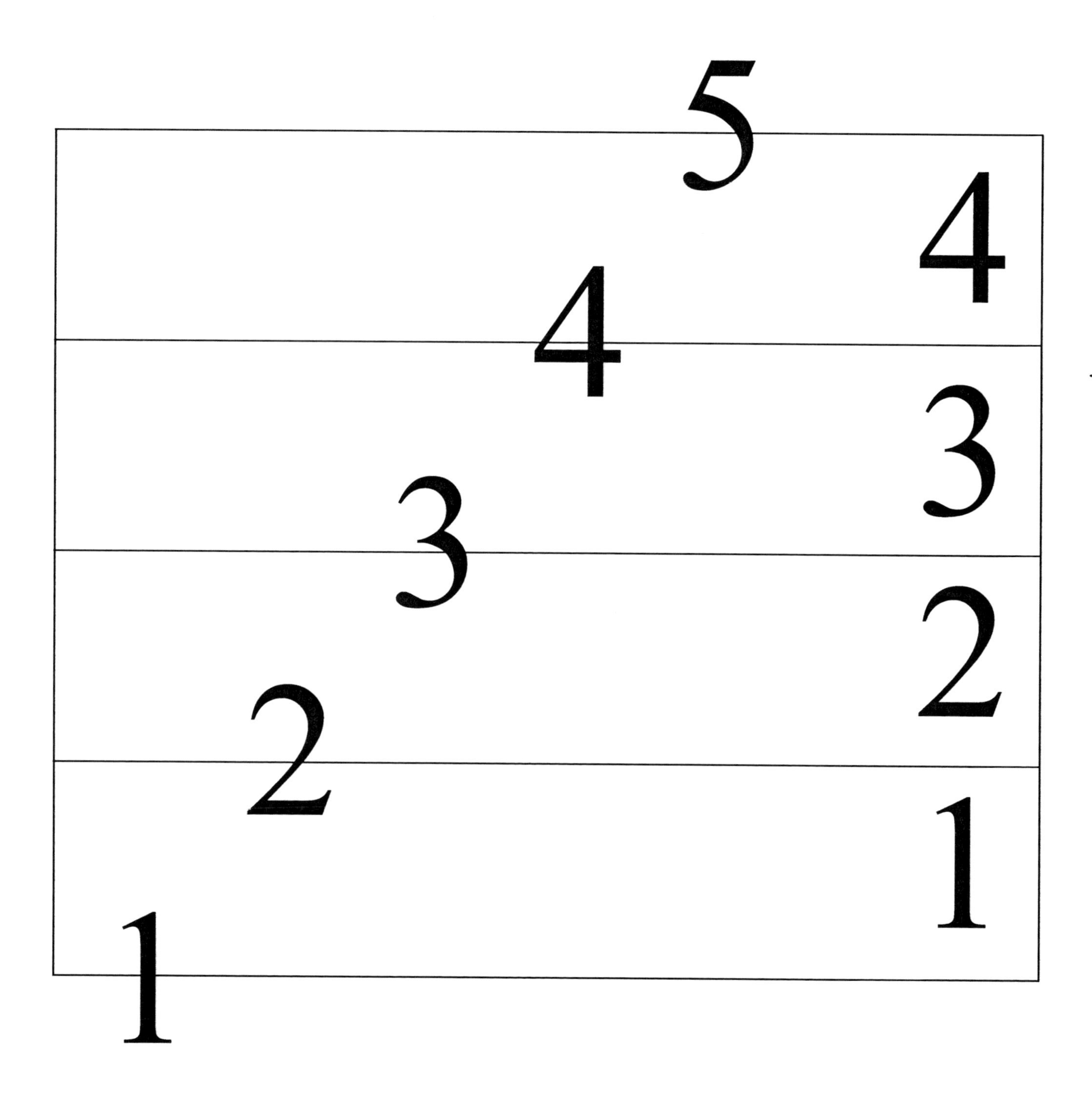

# The Ball Store

Fill up the four shelves with balls to sell. First connect the dots, than make more circles.
Decorate all of the balls with many colors.

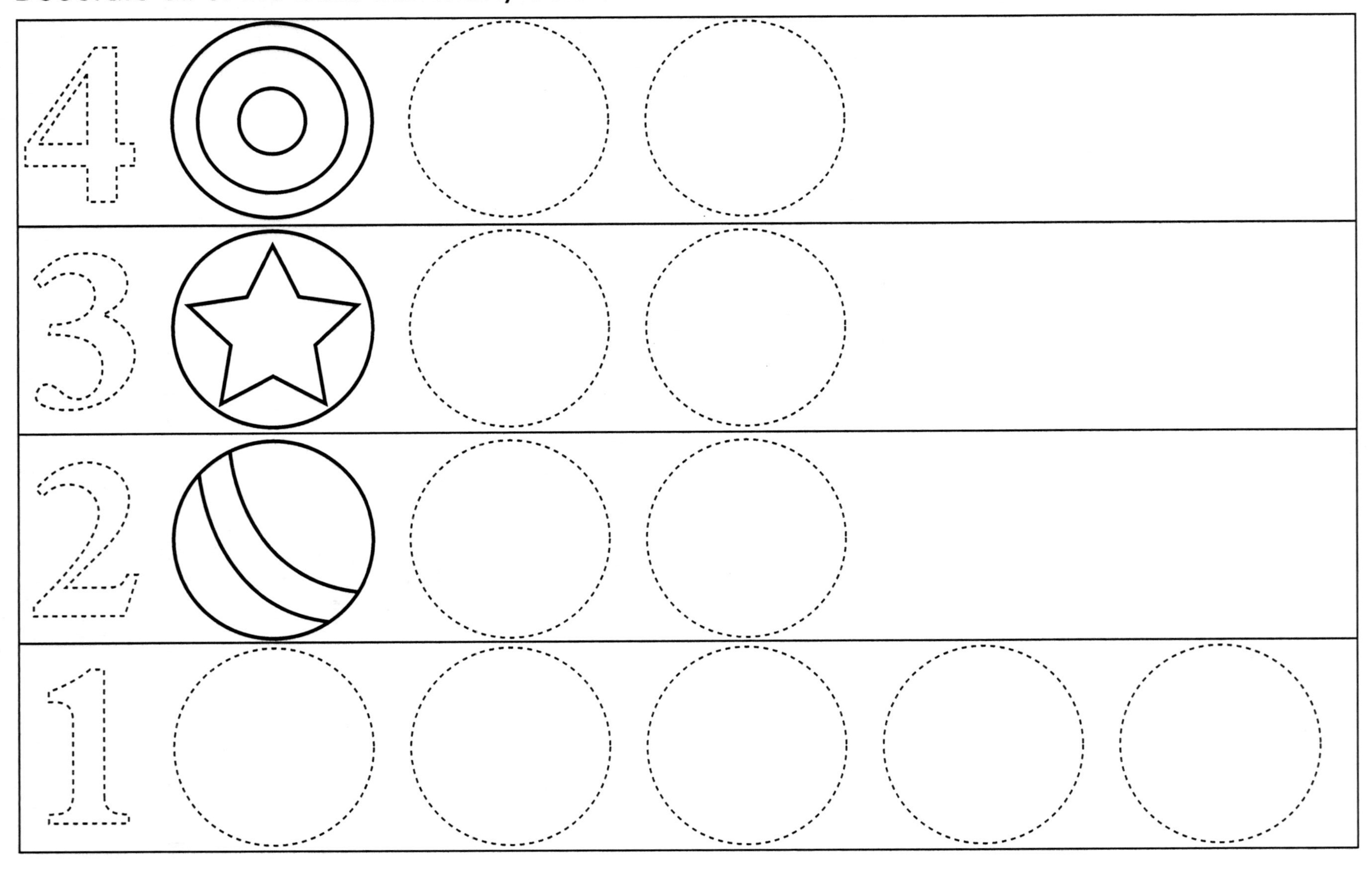

# S-T-A-F-F

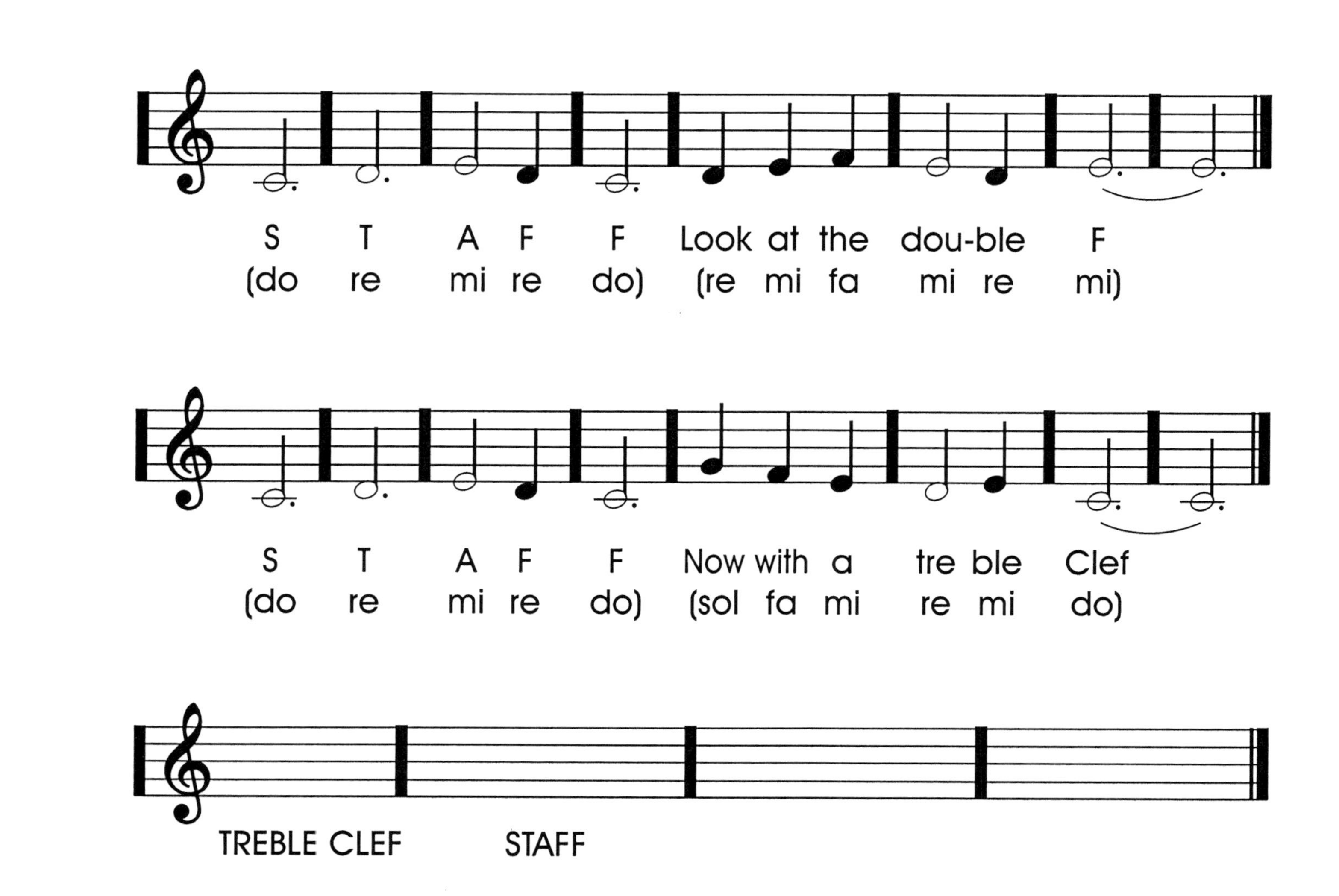


The teacher may wish to draw a diagram on the chalkboard.

# Do to Do

Do is first, it is so low
Re is next, the scale will grow
Mi, Mi, Mi, we tune our voice
Fa is fourth, for a nice choice
Sol is higher than the fourth
La is nice, so sing some more
Ti, hee, hee, it is so high
Do is way up in the sky.

Do Re, Mi, Fa, Sol, La, Ti Do

# Up to Do

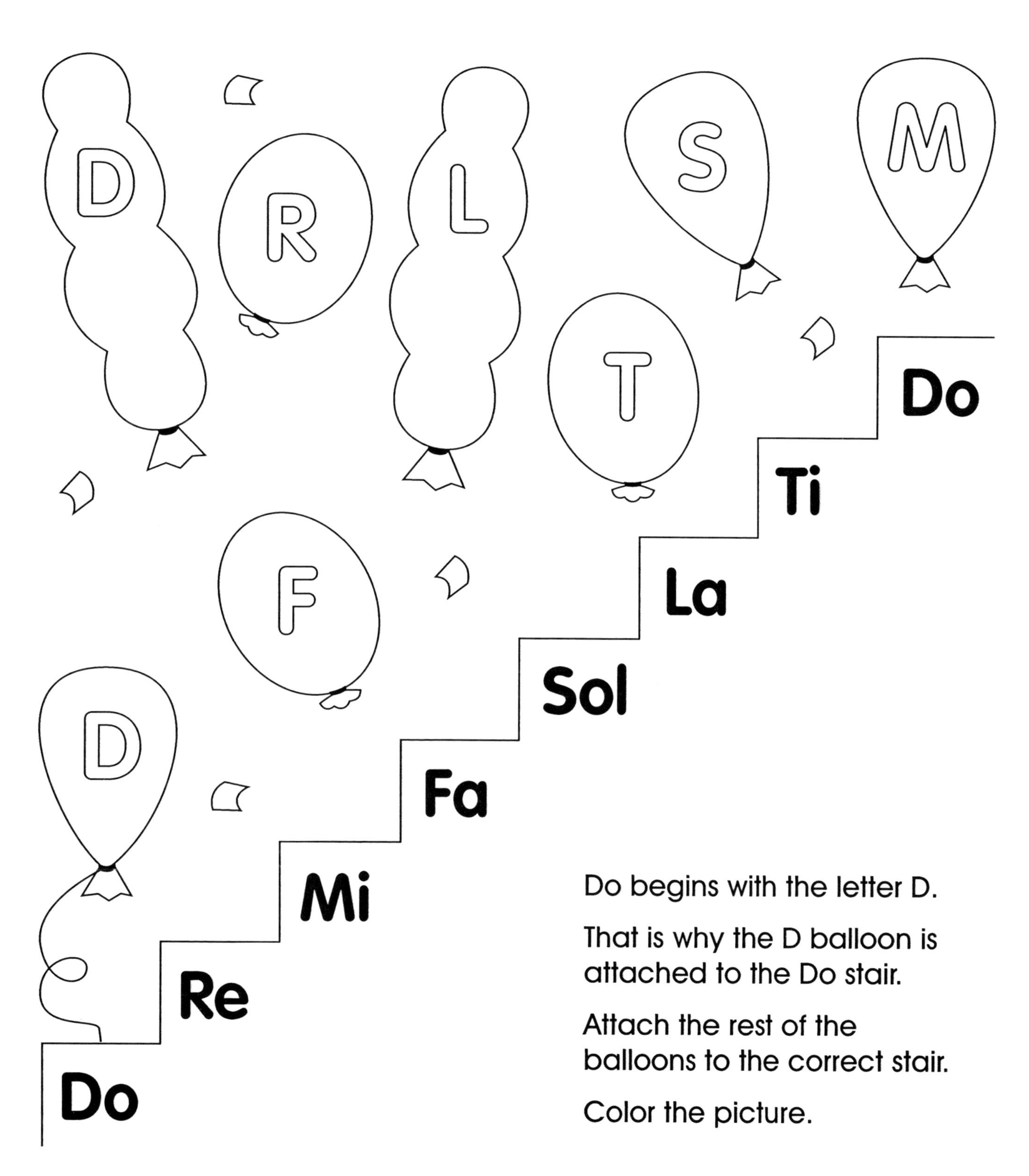


Do begins with the letter D.

That is why the D balloon is attached to the Do stair.

Attach the rest of the balloons to the correct stair.

Color the picture.

ISBN: 9781554950843

# Musical Letters

Color A, B, C, D, E, F, and G carefully. They are the only letters used in music. On the page print more A, B, C, D, E, F, Gs.

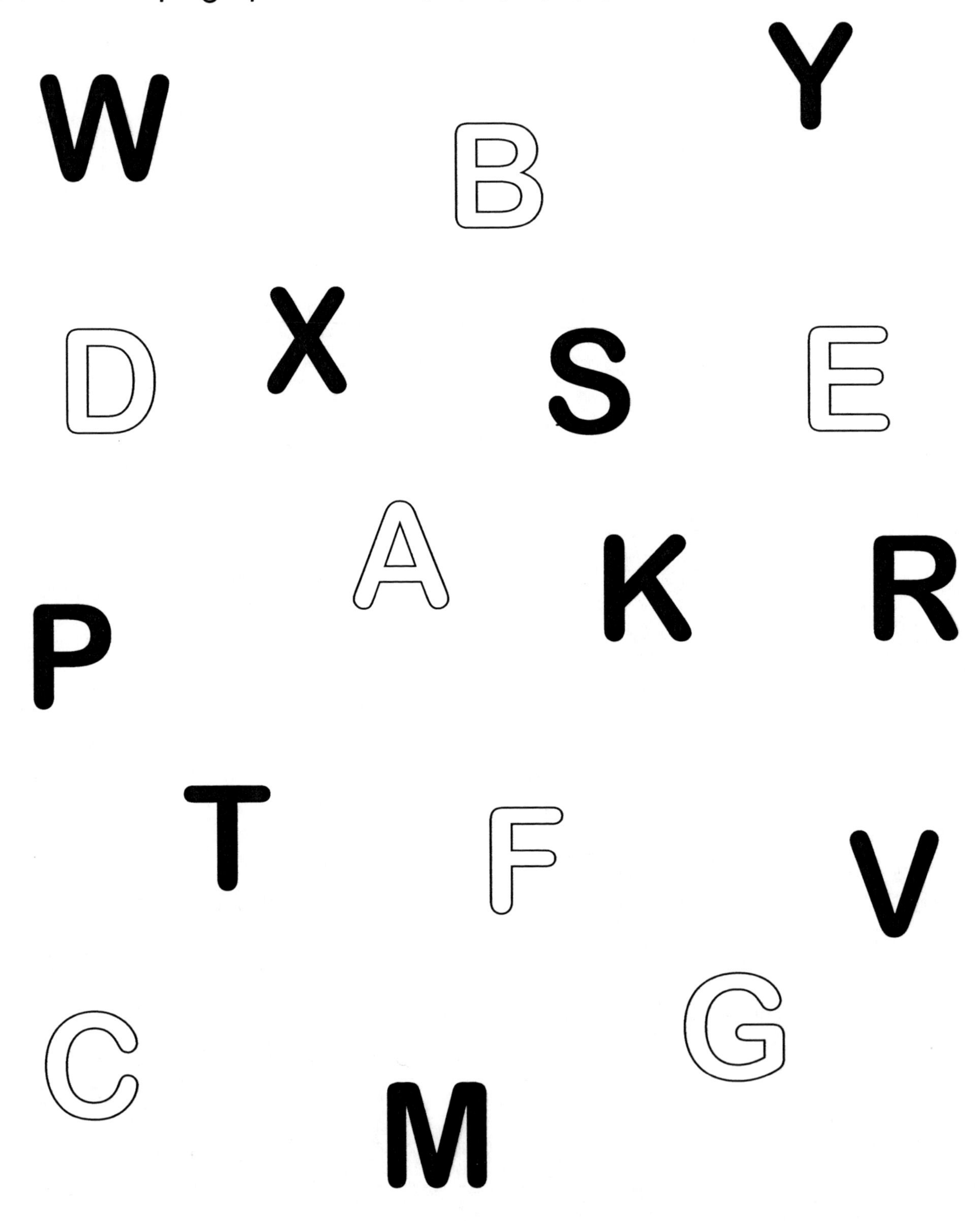

# Keyboard Craze

Neatly connect the broken lines and color the picture.

# The Secret Word

Circle all the letters below that are in the musical alphabet.
They are A, B, C, D, E, F, and G.
You will also find a secret word.

| | | | | | | | | |
|---|---|---|---|---|---|---|---|---|
| A | D | E | G | Y | F | B | C | A |
| B | E | B | C | C | B | E | G | C |
| A | B | D | E | E | D | O | E | D |
| D | C | F | G | F | A | B | C | A |
| A | F | D | B | G | C | D | G | E |
| B | G | F | U | A | E | B | F | G |
| C | A | F | C | B | D | C | E | B |

The secret word left uncircled is ______________.

# Answer Key

1. **Answer to Secret Word:** Y o u

2. **Answer to Dot to Dot:** Treble Clef

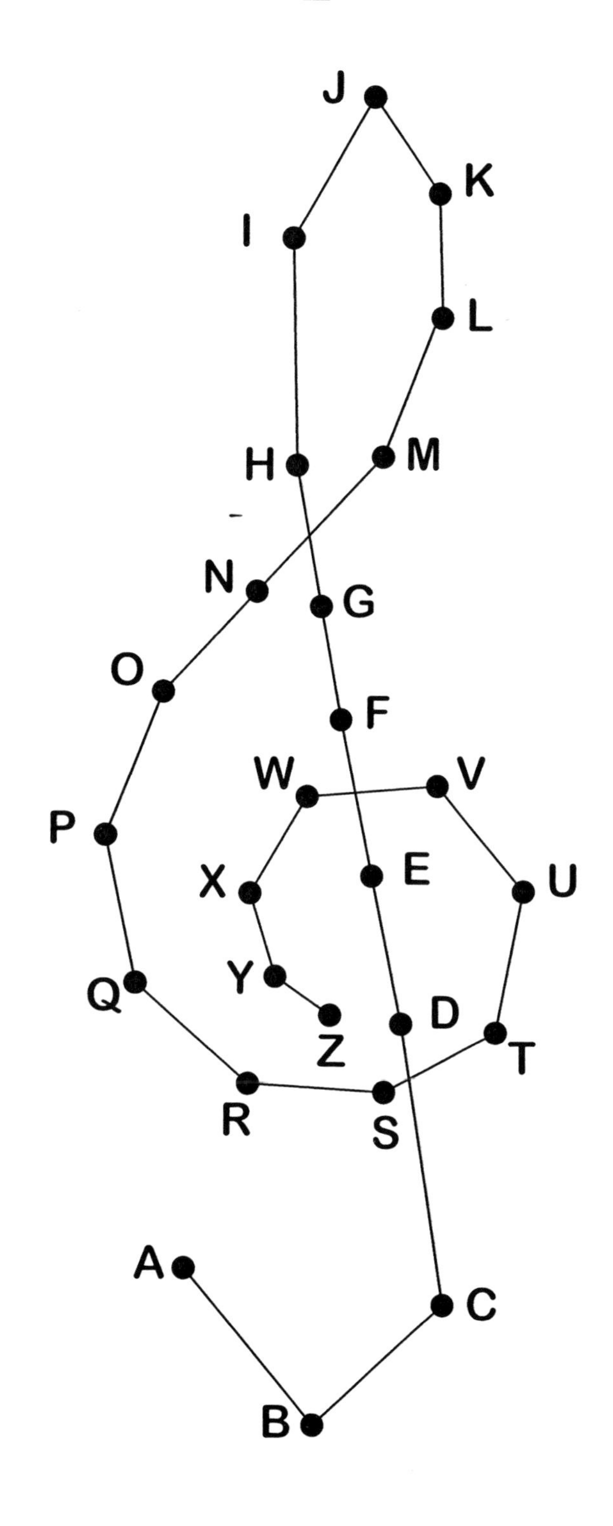

# Chopin and Me

Chopin played a percussion instrument called the piano at the age of four.

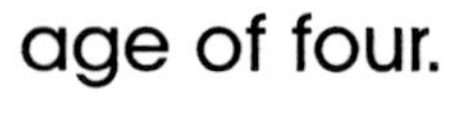

Do I play an instrument? ________________

ISBN: 9781554950843

Chopin didn't like eating a lot of foods.

Are there foods I don't Like? ______________________________

Chopin had a pet cat.

Do I have a pet? ______________________________

Chopin liked acting.

Do I like to act? ______________________________________________

Chopin lined his slippers up at his bed.

Do I wear slippers? ____________________________________________

ISBN: 9781554950843

Chopin played jokes on his friends. He would play soft music and then scare them with a loud bang.

Do I play jokes on my friends? ______________________________

Chopin's friends were Bach and Mozart. They were musicians too.

Do I have best friends? ______________________________

Teacher Notes:

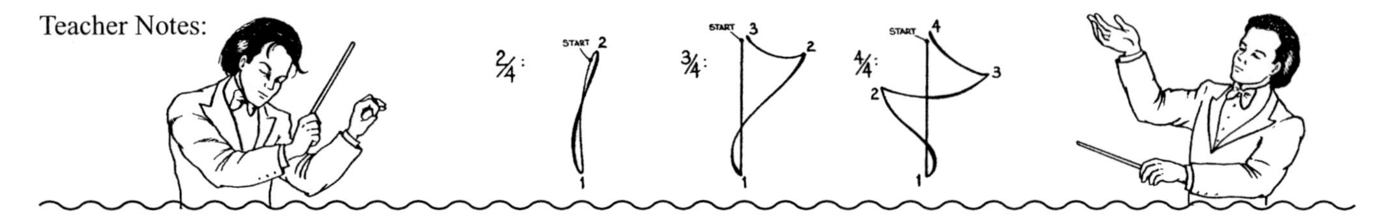


# Review Activities

- The holiday worksheets in the back of the unit are a review of all the facts learned.

- The number of ghosts have to be matched to the haunted house that has the same number of beats in it.

- The candy cane is to be colored by the music sign codes.

- My musical valentine is a word search but before the search begins, the heart must be finished with a solid line connecting all the same music signs.

- The four leaf clover is to be colored as follows : one beat sections are green and two beat sections are blue.

- The Easter egg is to be decorated with the music signs.

- The student must search for the music signs in the summer find and when it is completed, students could draw their own summer find on another page for another student to complete.

- Holiday worksheets are always exciting for the student. Their imaginations should run free and their creativity soar.

- The matching review is to recognize the music signs learned. It can be used as an optional test. The teacher could give directions such as circle the rests that get one beat in red. Color the keyboards blue, etc. Written instructions would be hard for some students in this grade; therefore the teacher using this sheet would have to decide what their students could be tested for.

- The sheet called Music in my World is for the student to relate music heard in the outside world.

# The Haunted House Hustle

The ghosts have to hurry home. They must get to the correct house. Match each group of ghosts to the house that have the same number of beats.

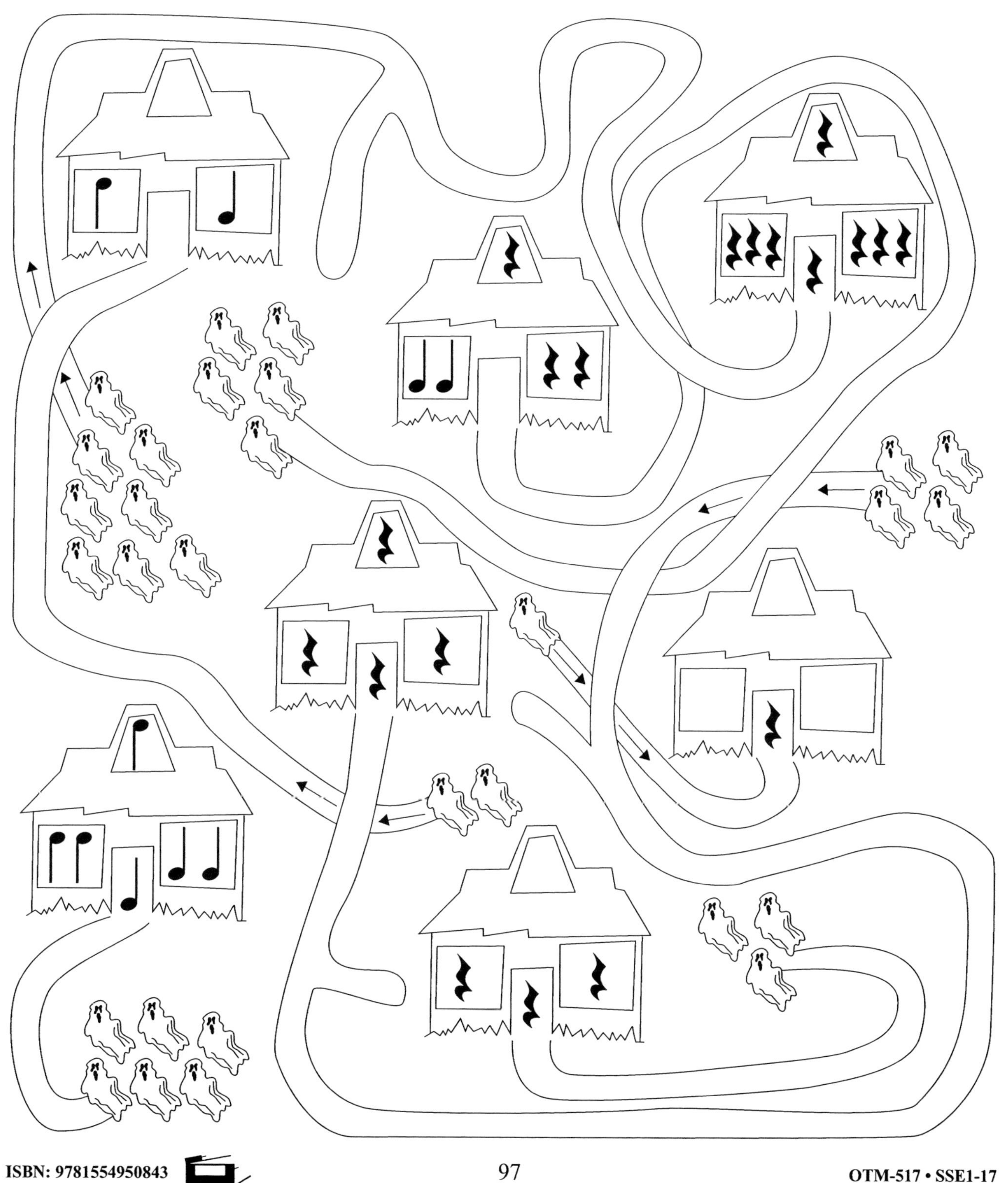

ISBN: 9781554950843

# Candy Cane Coloring

Color and finish the picture of the candy cane correctly.

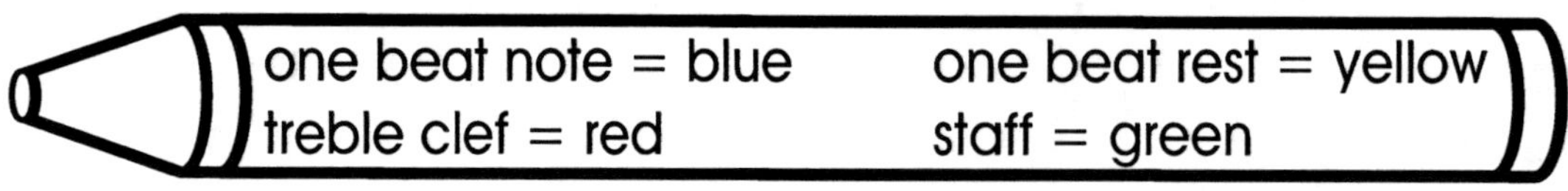

Draw more candy canes when you are done.

ISBN: 9781554950843 

# My Musical Valentine

Connect the music pictures with a solid line.

Circle these words in the valentine. one beat note rest treble clef staff drums cymbals

Do you see all the letters that are in the musical alphabet?

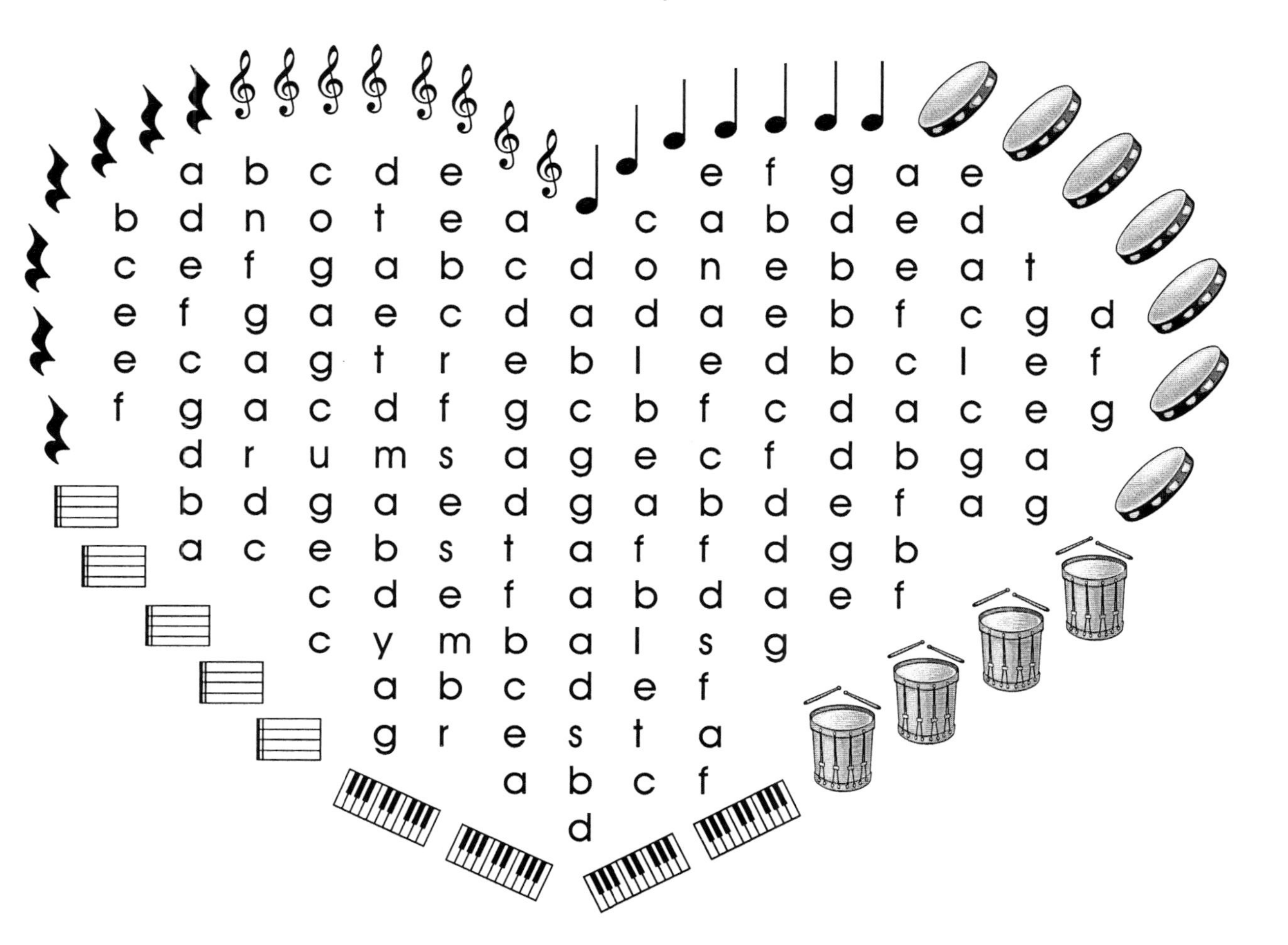


ISBN: 9781554950843

# How Lucky Are You?

Look for the one beat sections and color them green.

Look for the two beat sections and color them blue.

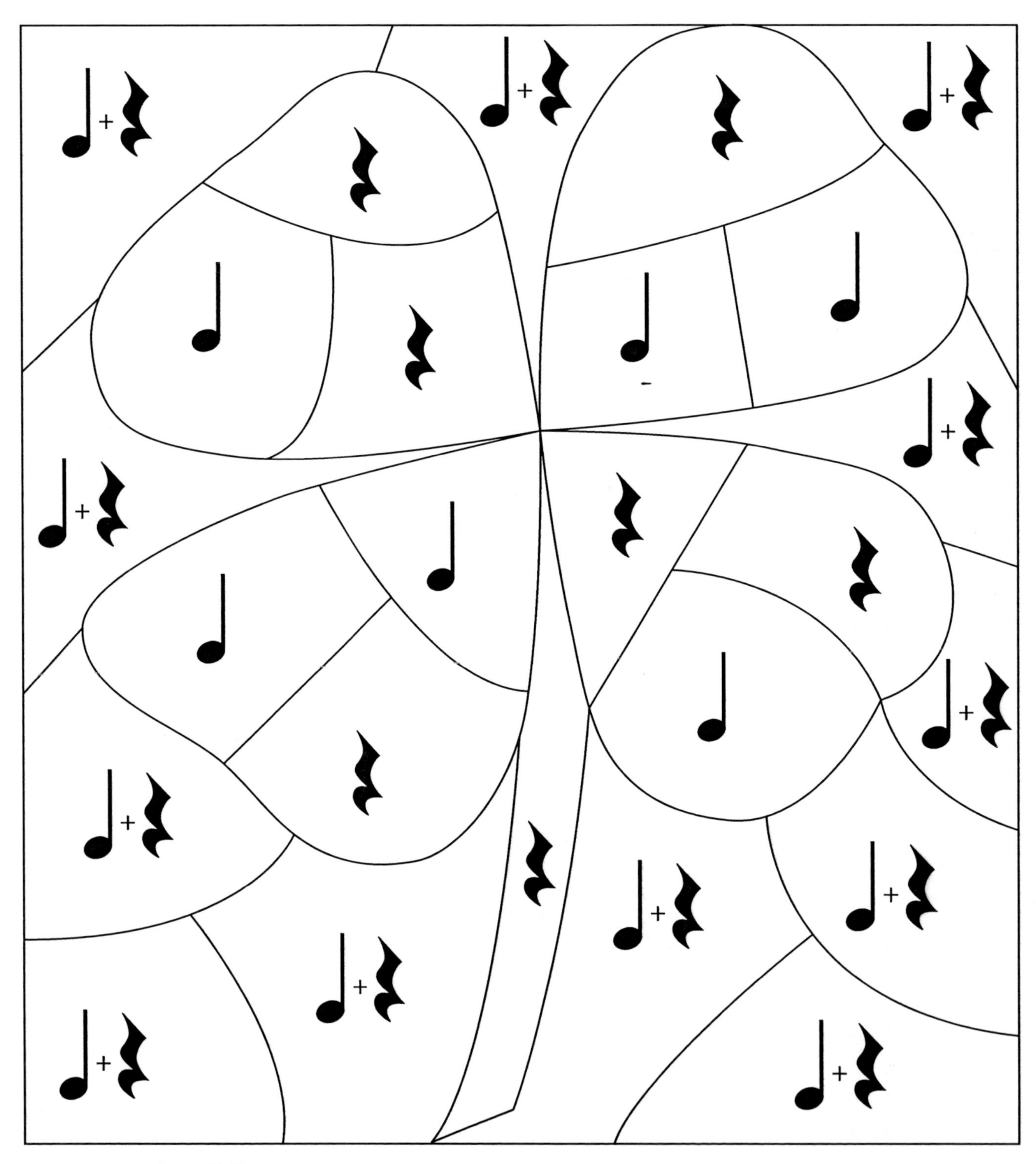

ISBN: 9781554950843

# Egg Decorating

Decorate the Easter egg with music signs.

Trace these signs and decorate the other egg using them.

ISBN: 9781554950843

# Summer Find

Outline all the music signs and instruments that you find in the picture and then color the picture.

ISBN: 9781554950843

# Match the Musical Picture with Its Twin

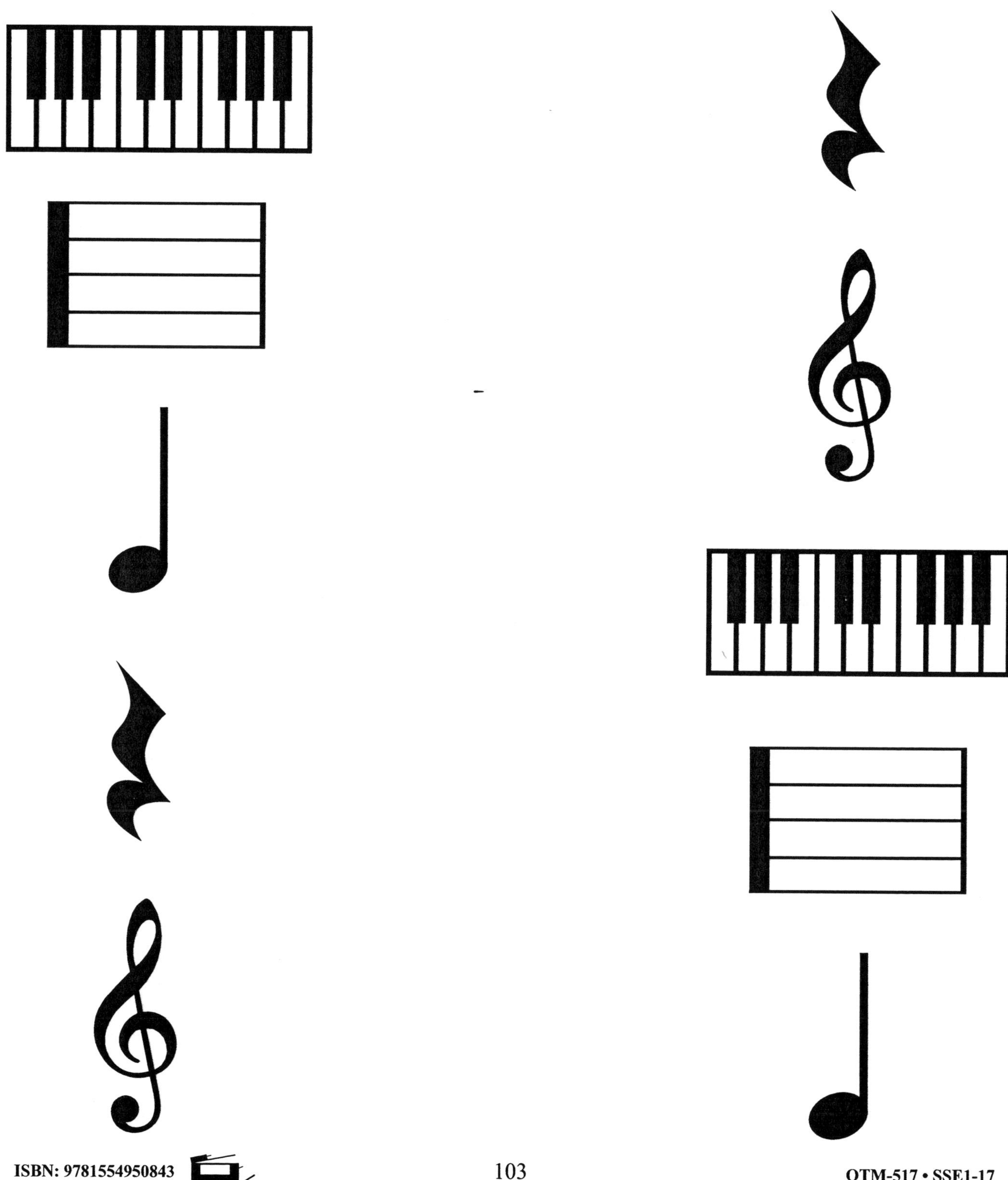

# My Favorite Musical Instrument

What is the name of your favorite musical instrument?

My favorite musical instrument is ______________________________.

In the box below draw a picture of it.

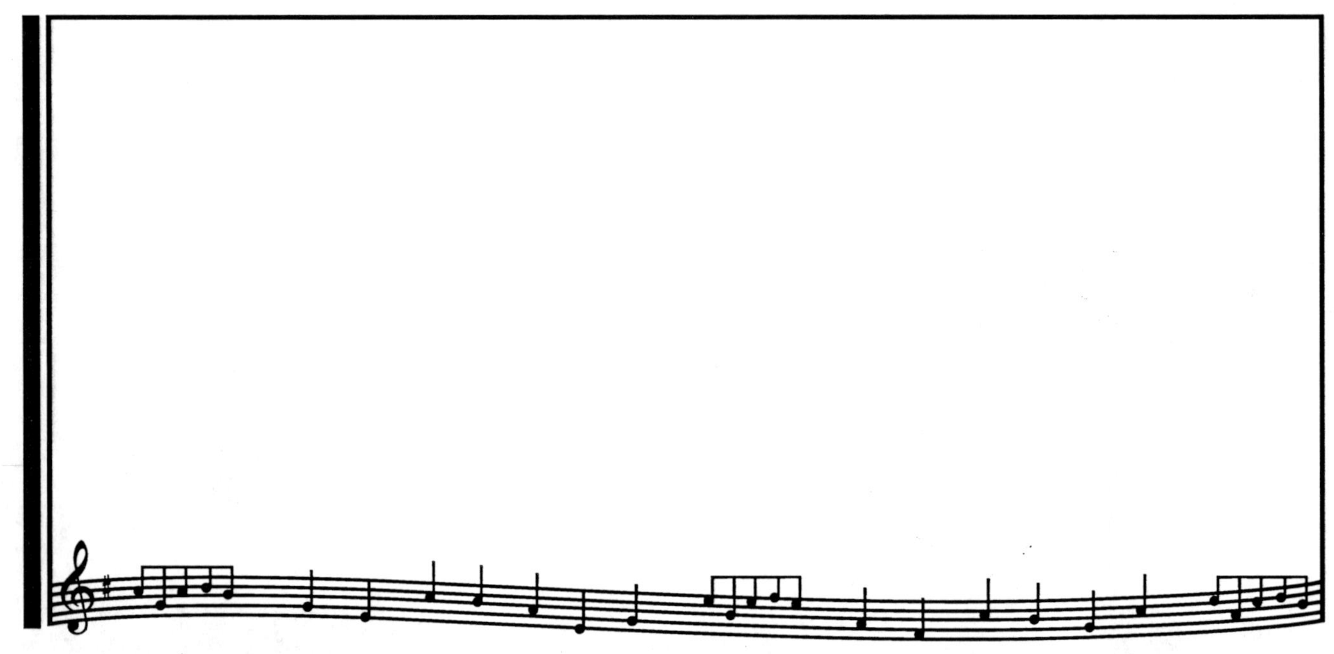

In the box below, draw a picture of yourself playing the instrument you like learning about the best.

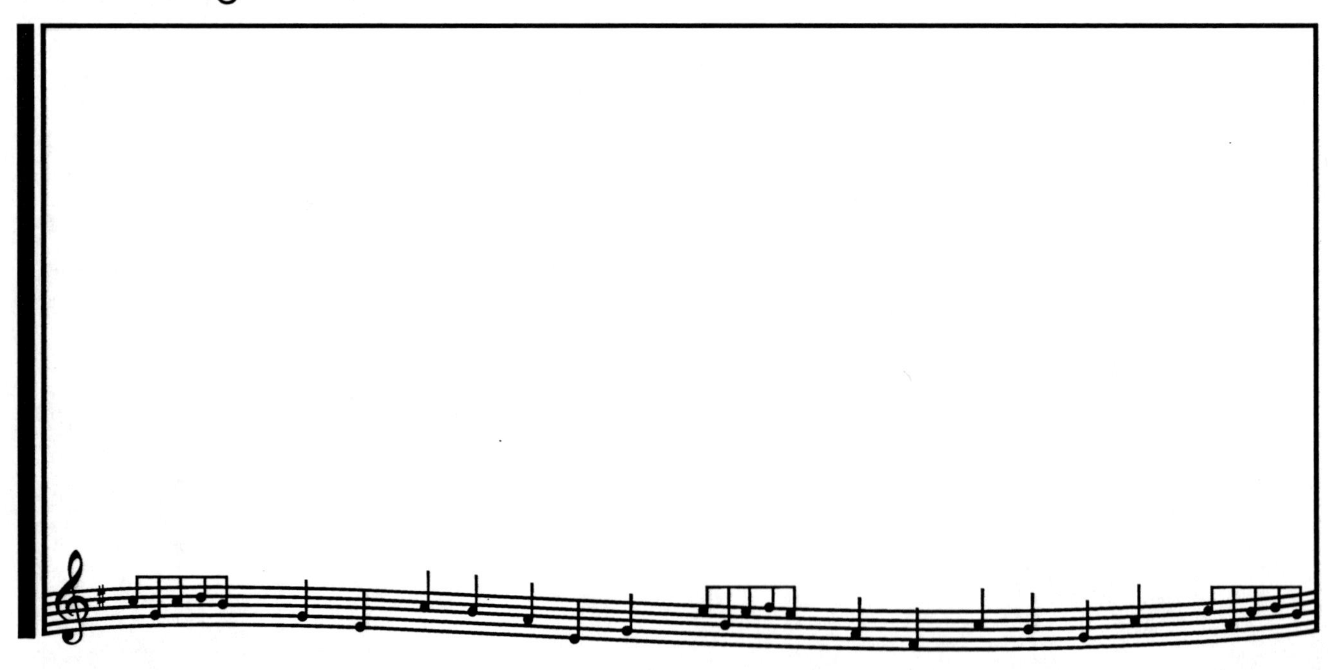

ISBN: 9781554950843

# Music In My World

I heard music playing ________________________________________.

I saw ________________________________________ playing music.

It was ________________________________________.

In the box below, draw a picture of what was making the music.

ISBN: 9781554950843

# Musical Games

## Game #1 - Spinner Quest

**Game Pieces:**
a spinner, the question and answer sheet, somewhere to score

**Preparations:**

1. The spinner needs to be assembled before playing. It is found on page 109.
2. The page with the large circle numbered 1 to 14 must be cut out and glued onto the pie plate.
3. The spinner, which can be made from plastic, needs to be attached with a duo tang clip in the center. This spinner, which is shaped like an arrow, should be able to spin and point to the numbers which coincide with the question sheet.
4. Score cards are needed, or the score can be kept on the chalkboard.

**Playing the Game:**

1. This game can be played as a class or split into groups.
2. The first student spins.
3. The teacher then reads the corresponding question.
4. The group or individual must answer correctly for one point.
5. Individually, players are eliminated with a wrong answer. As a group, teams must reach a certain number of points to win.

## Game #2 - Musical Memory

1. This is a memory card game.
2. Pages 110 and 111 need to be photocopied, mounted on a sturdy backing, and cut to assemble the cards for the game.
3. The cards are then lined up face down in any order and player one turns over two random cards to try and match a pair.
4. If they don't match, the cards are returned face down and the next player takes a turn.
5. If a pair is matched, the pair is kept and the player takes an additional turn until a matched pair does not turn up.
6. The player with the most pairs wins the game.
7. Do not include the old composer card for this game.

# Musical Games

## Game #3 - The Old Composer

1. The same cards, as in Game #2, are used for this game, including the Old Composer card.
2. Players are dealt all the cards.
3. Player #1 asks the player on the left for a card that he/she has in his/her hand and tries to get a matching pair. If the player does, the player goes again. If the player doesn't, the next player plays.
4. The pairs of cards are displayed in front of them and counted at the end.
5. The player with the most pairs wins the game.
6. The player left with the old composer card becomes "The Old Composer."
7. Make sure if you are adding additional copies of the cards that you have only one old composer card so there isn't a matching pair.

## Game #4 - Go Rest

1. This is also a card game, using the cards with the rests.
2. They also need to be assembled.
3. The object of the game is to get four of the same cards for a set which gives one point.
4. Four copies of page 112 are needed for a full deck of cards.
5. Players are dealt seven cards.
6. The rest of the cards are put in the middle face down, in a pile.
7. The first player asks the player on the left for a certain card. The player must give all of the cards in his/her hand that add up to the number of rests asked for.
8. If the player is successful, he/she can ask for a different one until the player asked doesn't have that card and says "Go Rest."
9. Player one takes a card from the middle and it is player two's turn.
10. When four of the same cards are collected, the set is placed down in front of the player.
11. The highest number of sets wins the game.

## Suggestions

1. The games will teach the students to recognize music signs, instruments and the value of a one beat rest.
2. You may want extra sets of cards because they tend to wear out after time. If the students are having problems recognizing the signs, you could also color code the same cards to make it easier.
3. If you are working in groups, you may want to have other materials such as reproducibles and worksheets available in case some games take longer than others to play.

# Spinner Quest

GAME #1

## Questions and Answers

1. The kind of instrument that has black and white keys that you press is called a _______________. (keyboard)

2. The instruments that have a twin and you crash them both together are called _______________. (cymbals)

3. The instruments that have a twin and you shake them are called ____________. (maracas)

4. This instrument is round and you tap it or shake it when it is played. It is called a _______________. (tambourine)

5. The instrument that you beat and it helps to keep the beat in a song is a _______________. (drum)

6. The instrument that is shaped with three sides and makes a soft ting sound is called a _______________. (triangle)

7. The instrument that has seven notes like a keyboard but is made of metal is called _______________. (bells)

8. The black note gets _______________ beat. (one)

9. The squiggly rest gets _______________ beat. (one)

10. In singing, it comes after do, re, mi, _______________. (fa)

11. The word for high and low is _______________. (pitch)

12. It is made up of five lines and four spaces. It is called a _______________. (staff)

13. The seven letters used in music are _______________. (A, B, C, D, E, F, G)

14. One of Chopin's friend's name was _______________. (Bach or Mozart)

## Spinner

GAME #1

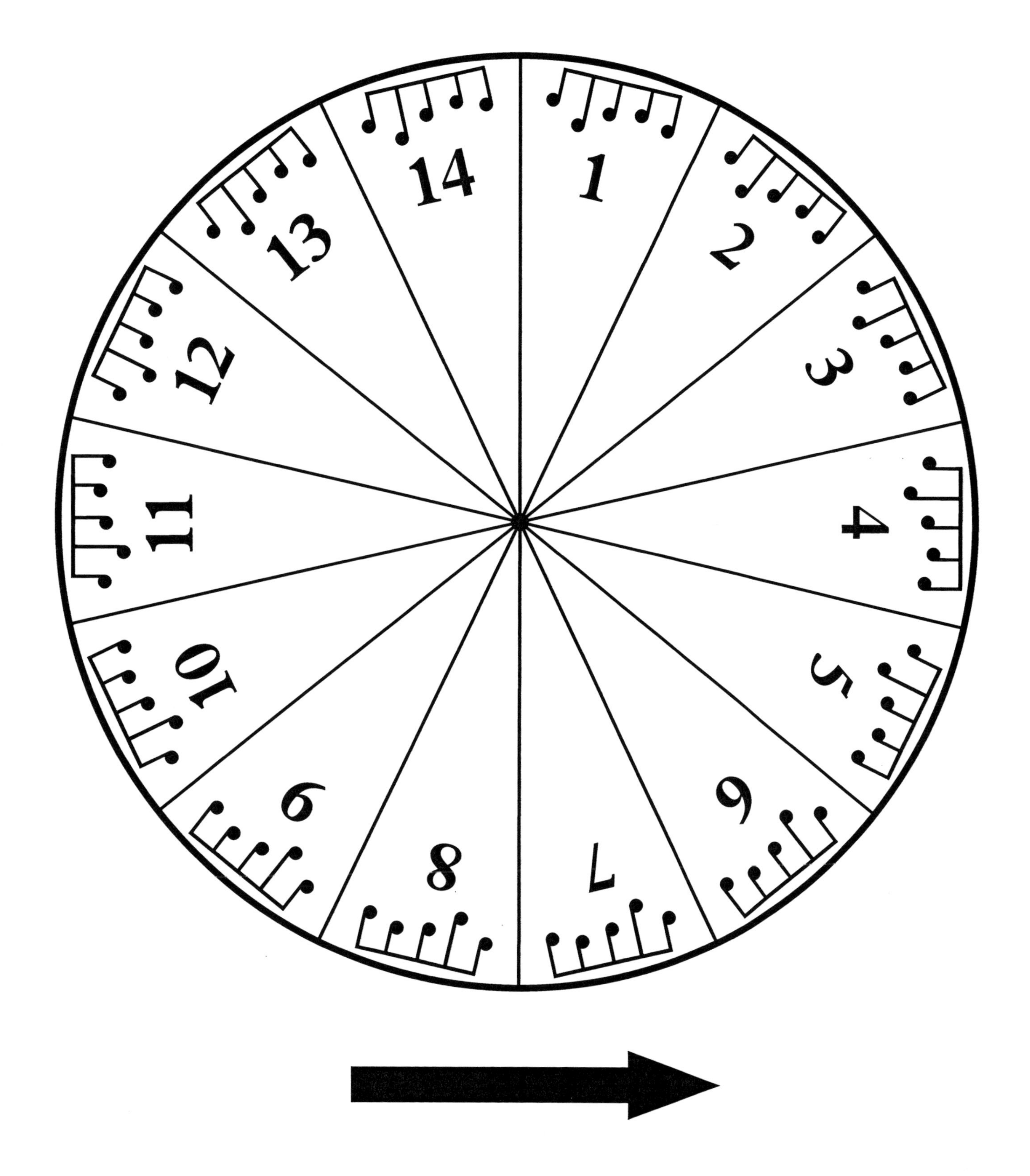


ISBN: 9781554950843

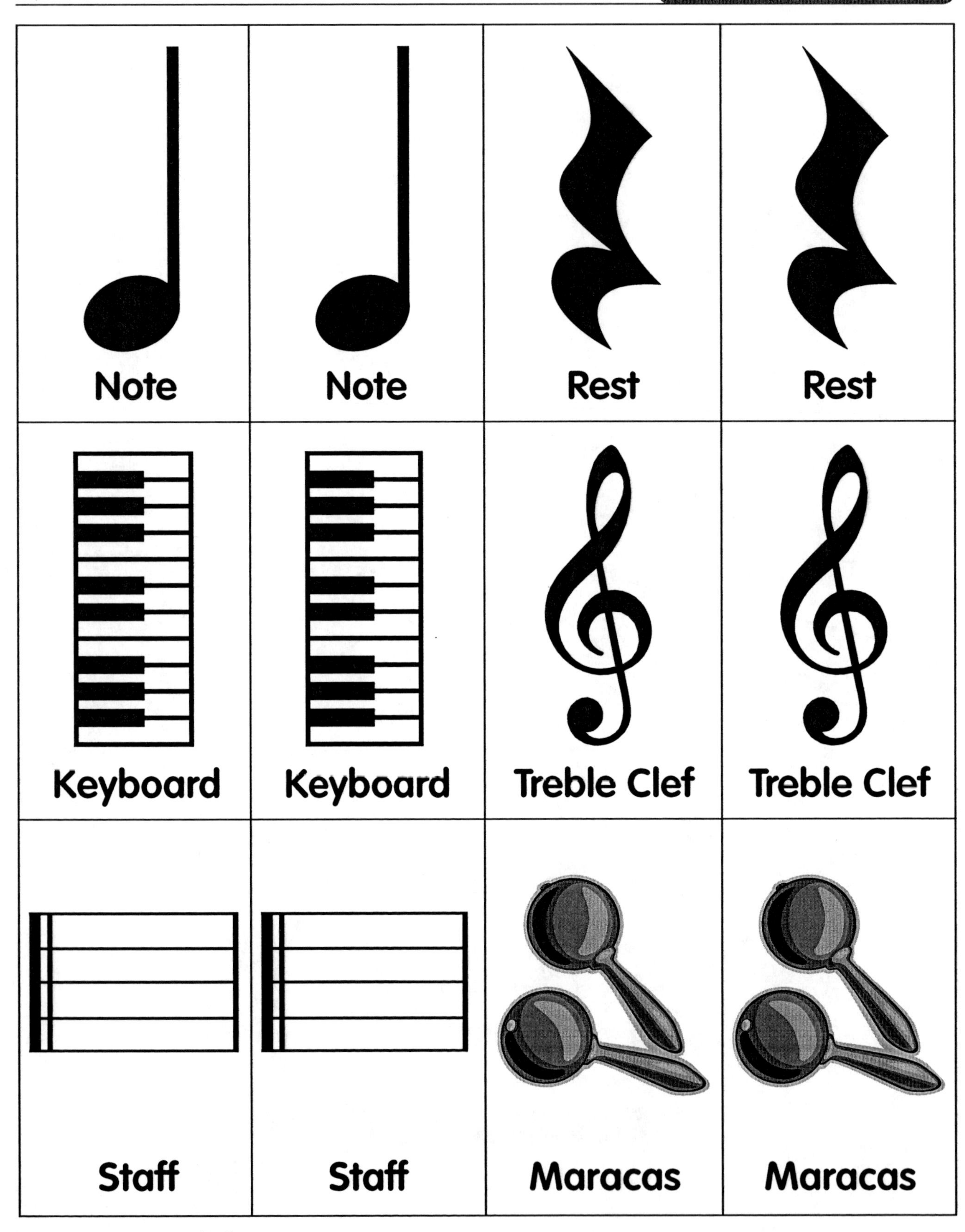
Note
Note
Rest
Rest
Keyboard
Keyboard
Treble Clef
Treble Clef
Staff
Staff
Maracas
Maracas

# Cards

GAMES #2 & #3

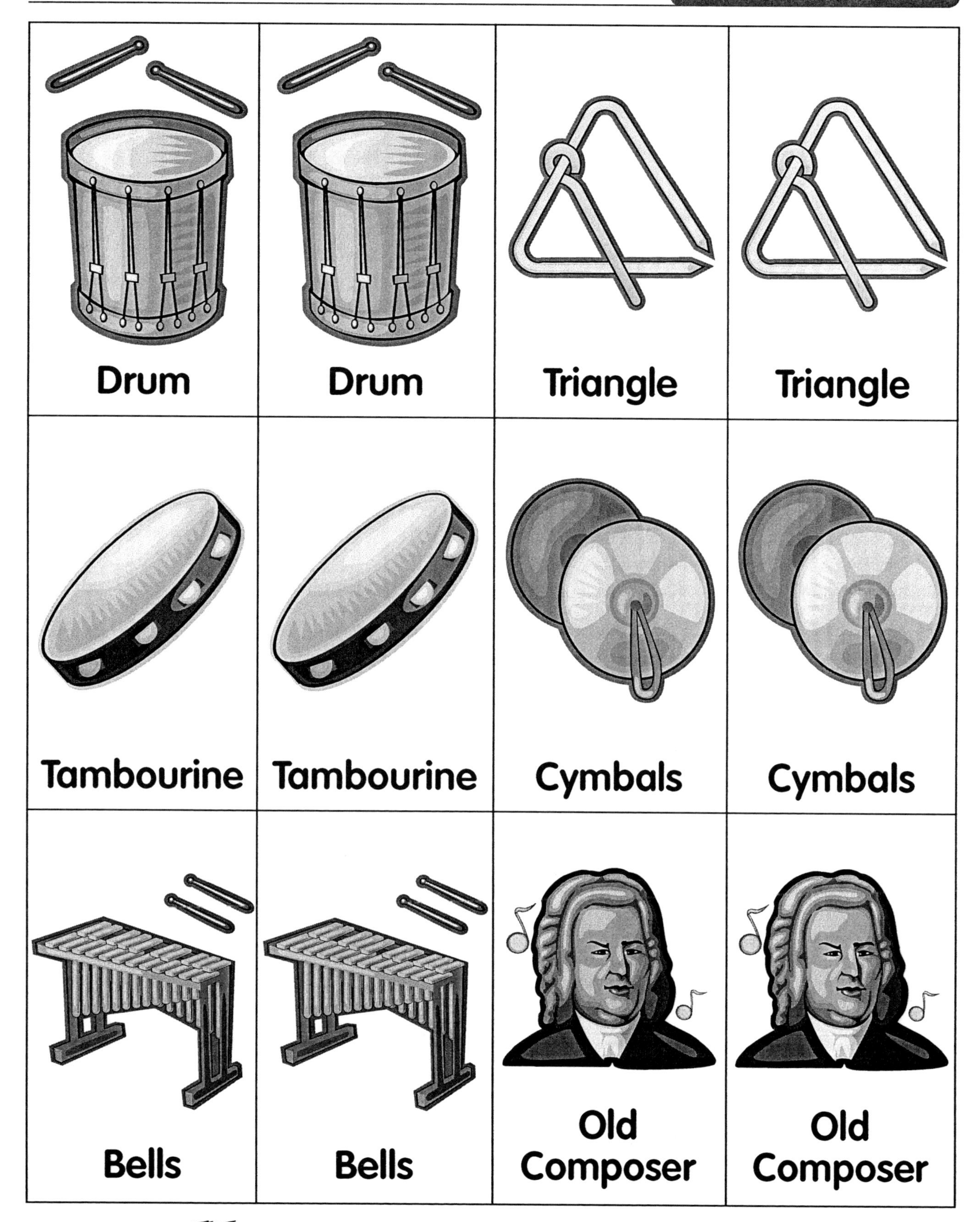

# Go Rest! Cards

GAME #4

Teacher Notes:

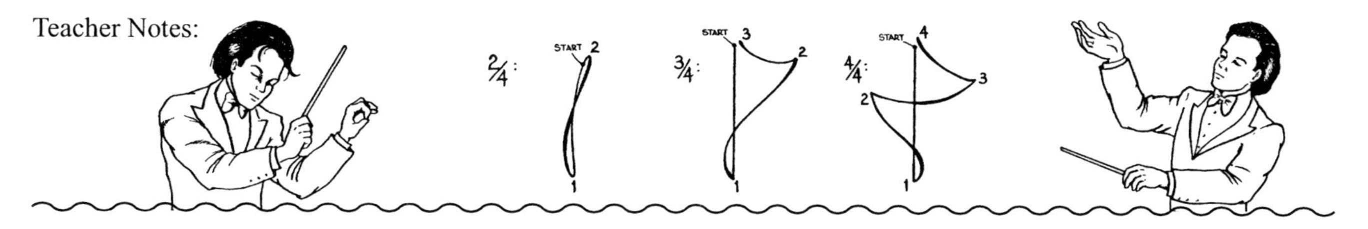


# Developing Music Skills in Grade 2

**Introduction:**

The activities in this book have three intentions:

- to encourage students to be creative.
- to encourage their enjoyment of music.
- to educate them in the field of music.

Since creativity is very important in music, there will be variety in the way the work will be accomplished. The students should enjoy this program and take a positive approach to music. They may like to take the information home or to other environments. Music is everywhere and is a universal language. The students might be amazed with the effect that it has on peoples' lives and the endless variety of music that exists.

The concepts introduced are the

- stringed instruments
- the two beat note
- the treble clef
- the double bar line
- the musical alphabet
- the one beat note
- the two beat rest
- the bass clef
- pitch
- singing do to do
- the one beat rest
- the staff
- the bar line
- A, B, C, D, E, F, G
- the composer Mozart

1. Each exercise will have a main point or idea, a sign to learn or a musical activity to finish.
2. If there are small dots, the student is to connect the dots to help form letters, numbers, signs or directions.
3. A variety of materials is necessary such as crayons, markers, colored paper or other available supplies.
4. The students could make a musical booklet to keep their work altogether. This could be used as a reference.
5. When their booklets or their activities are completed, the students can receive a certificate with or without testing, depending upon the teacher.
6. The games will re-enforce the knowledge learned.
7. A prize board is a great incentive but is optional.

Teacher Notes:

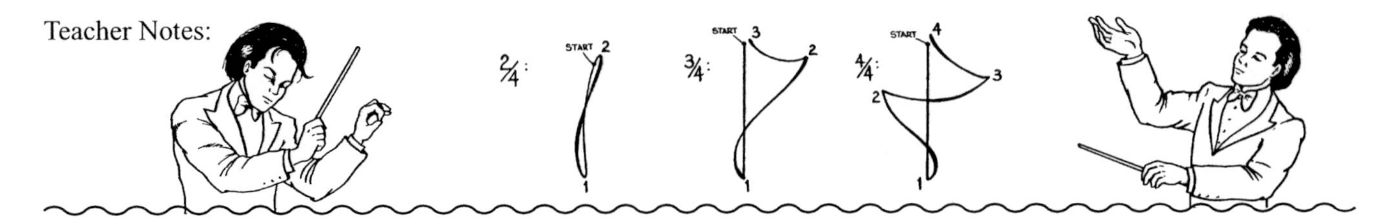


# List of Materials

- Worksheets will be done with a variety of coloring materials.

- Crayons of different textures and colors, markers or pencil crayons of different shades are very effective.

- Graphite pencils will be needed for drawing.

- To make the tissue box harp, a tissue box will be needed for each student with the center hole punched out, coloring, painting, and cut and paste materials, five elastics of different thickness for each student, and staples.

- For the games you will need construction paper, glue, a score page, a foil paper plate, a duotang, - and an arrow made of plastic.

- Tapping sticks or other tapping instruments could be used to accompany songs to be sung in the classroom.

- The best materials to be used for the reproducibles are crayons of some sort. If paper is used over the top of the reproducible, regular crayons are great to shade on the top sheet to make designs. If the reproducibles are to be traced, students will require pencil crayons or pencils and regular crayons to color.

- Incentives, such as prizes for a prize board are great for encouragement. The prizc board would have to be prepared with construction paper and coloring material. Prizes could include music stickers, erasers or small items.

ISBN: 9781554950843  

Teacher Notes:

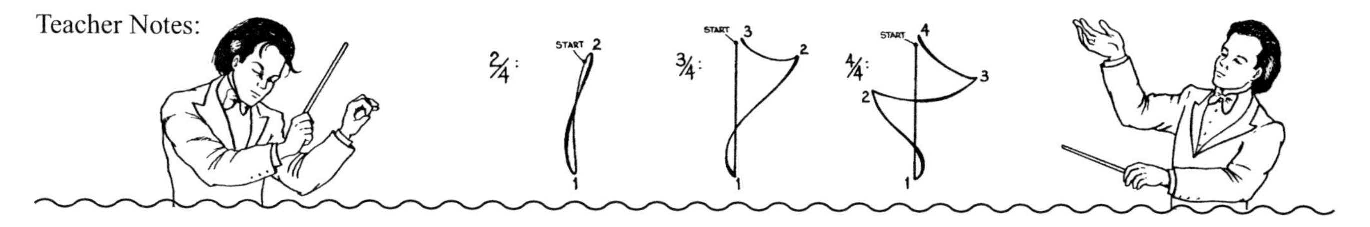


# Teaching Suggestions

Any of the following ideas can be used in the classroom to motivate student interest in music.

- Display signs or musical characters in the classroom.
- Display pictures of various musical instruments and discuss their shape and sound.
- Be familiar with the music terms at this grade level.
- Try having the children work individually, in groups or as a whole class.
- If working in groups, rotate groups at different work stations.
- Provide different types of crayons, colored pencils, and materials for student usage.
- Make the harps before doing the songs in the classroom.
- Students with some knowledge of music should be grouped with students who do not have any knowledge of music.
- Assemble games and boards ahead of time.
- Encourage students to think of music at home and in other environments.
- Encourage creativity and enjoyment at all times.
- If possible, bring instruments into the classroom.
- Listen to different types of music during a quiet time or as a break from work.

ISBN: 9781554950843

Teacher Notes:

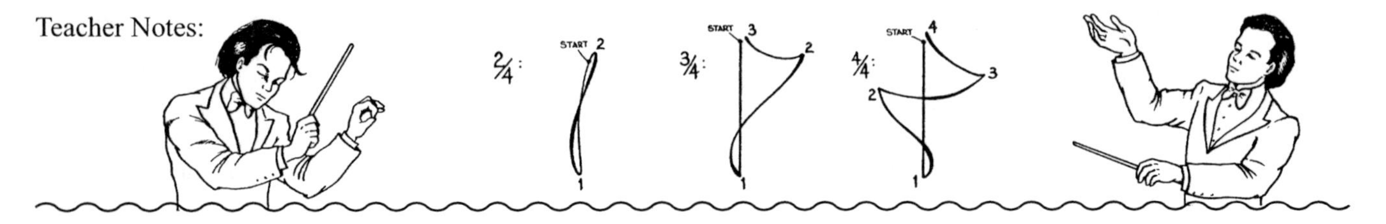


# Music Glossary

**String Instruments:** These are a family of instruments that are played by strumming or plucking strings. This can be done with a bow, a pick or the musician's fingers. Technically, a piano, is also a string instrument but the strings are hit by a wooden hammer. It is often not part of the strings in an orchestra. In this book, the main focus is on the violin, the viola, the cello, the bass, and the harp. This is from the smallest and highest sounding to the largest and the lowest sounding.

**Notes:** When you see a note, there needs to be a sound made by an instrument or a voice.

**Rests:** Rests are periods of silence. When resting for one beat, there needs to be a period of silence for the count of one. When resting for two beats, there needs to be a period of silence for the count of two.

**One Beat:** One beat is one count, like the tick of a clock.

**Two Beats:** Tick, tock would be two beats or two counts.

**High and Low Pitch:** Some instruments play in a higher range or pitch just like some voices have a higher range or pitch. The high range uses the treble clef and the lower range uses other clefs, learned at a later time.

**Treble Clef:** The clef is used for the highest pitched instruments or the higher end of keyboard instruments. The middle point of the treble clef centers all round the G line of the staff and sometimes can be called the G Clef.

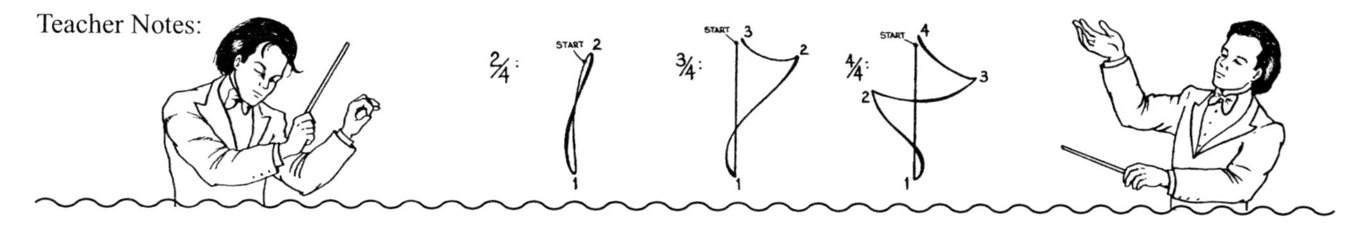


# Music Glossary

**Bass Clef:** The clef used for the lowest instruments or the low end of the keyboard. The bass clef circles around the F line and is sometimes called the F clef.

**Bar Line:** The bar line is a vertical line separating music into sections. These sections are based on the timing of the song

**Double Bar Line:** This is a double bar line or two bar lines at the end of the song.

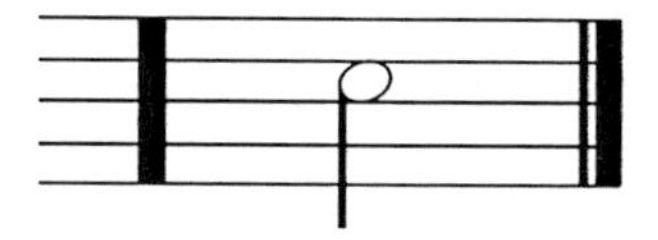

**Staff:** The five lines and four spaces that music is written on. Sometimes more than one staff is connected and they will be called staves.

**Composer:** A composer is a songwriter from the past or present.

Teacher Notes:

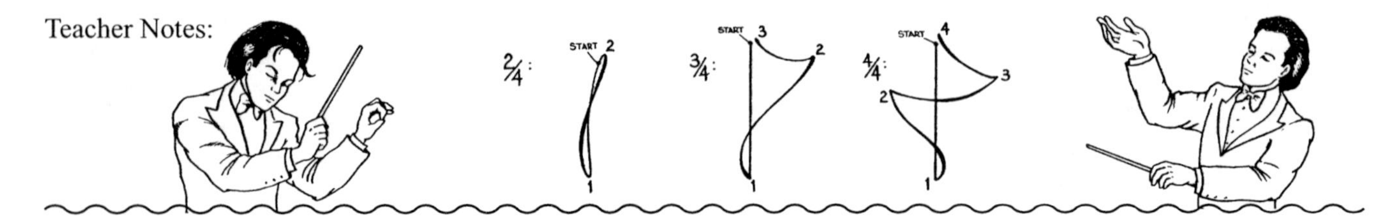


# Musical Elements

This section deals with the following musical elements:

- the one beat note
- the one beat rest
- the two beat note
- the two beat rest
- the treble clef
- the bass clef
- music signs

1. There are two display sheets which can be displayed in the classroom or photocopied and added to the students' music booklets. See page 119 and 120.

2. The exercise on the one and two beat notes should be done after explaining what one beat is. This is explained on the page called "Is it 1 or 2?" on page 121. It is then followed by the exercise.

3. The next five worksheets are a combination of addition questions and coloring the treble clef, the bass clef, and one and two beat notes and rests.

4. The reproducibles that are to be used for tracing or coloring over should be cut out and glued onto cardboard at this point. The teacher may want to make many copies of the reproducibles as they wear out quickly. This should be a fun and creative activity for the students. It is such a flexible exercise because it can be done individually or in groups. The reproducible tracings completed by the students could be made into insects, other creatures or garden flowers. They will spark the imagination of the student. Cards can also be made for special occasions.

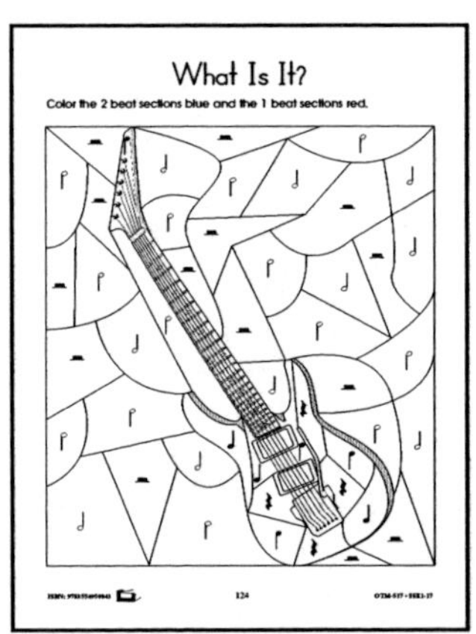


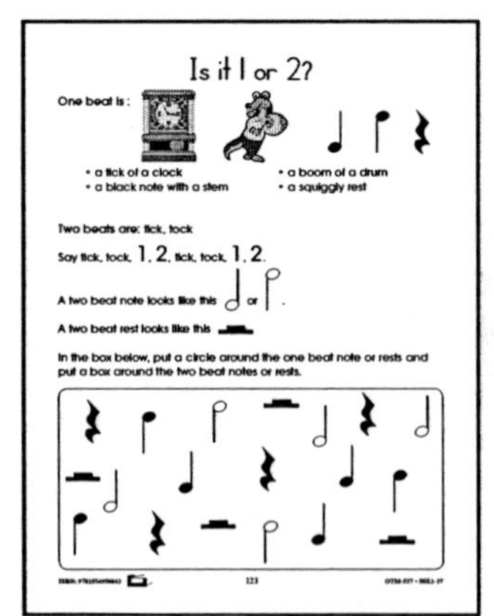


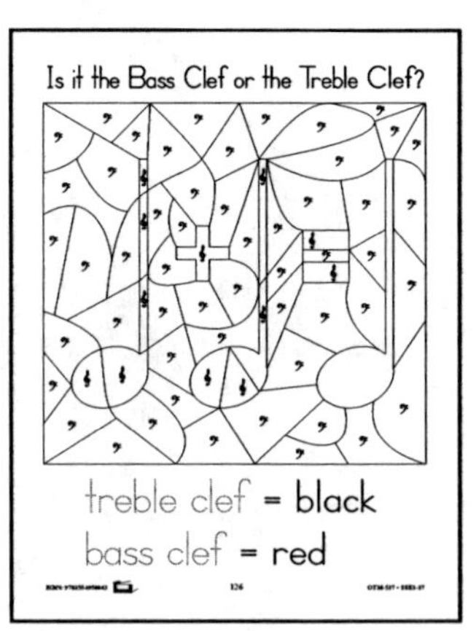

# Musical Notes

## The One Beat Note and Rest

Note Note Rest

## The Two Beat Note and Rest

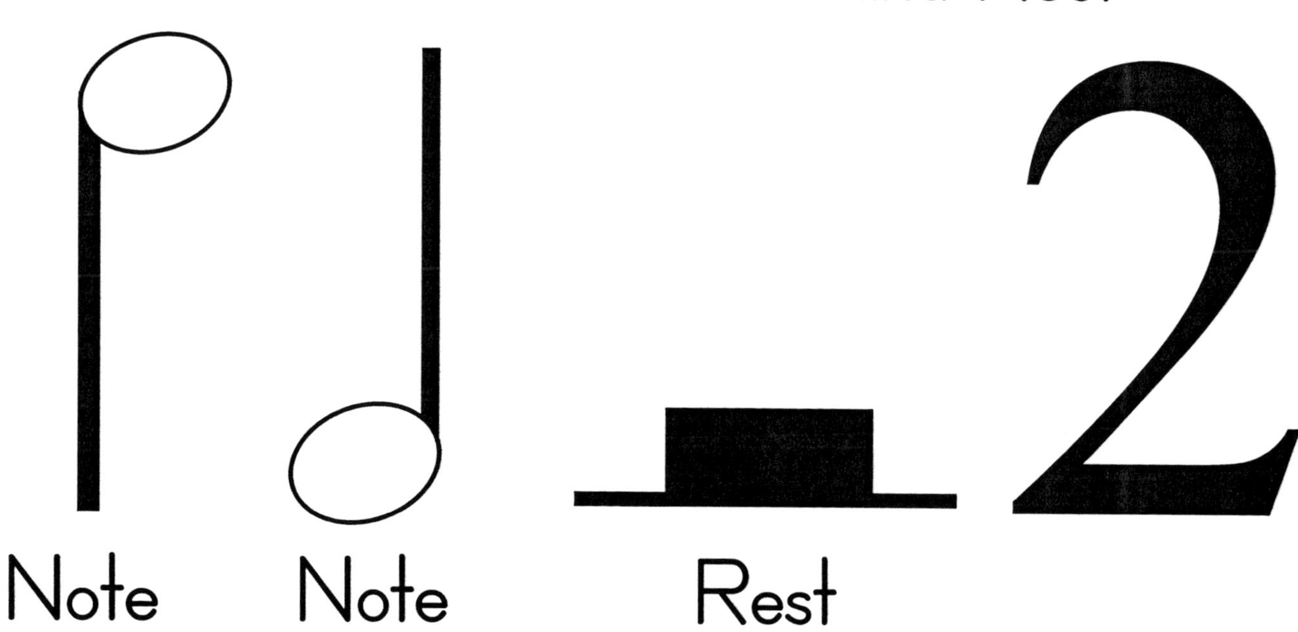


Note Note Rest

# Music Signs

Bass Clef

Treble Clef

The Staff

Bar Line

Double Bar Line

ISBN: 9781554950843

# Is it I or 2?

**One beat is :**

- a tick of a clock
- a black note with a stem
- a boom of a drum
- a squiggly rest

**Two beats are:** tick, tock

Say tick, tock, 1, 2, tick, tock, 1, 2.

A two beat note looks like this 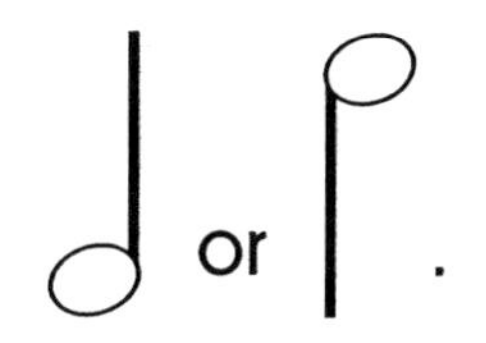 .

A two beat rest looks like this ▬ .

In the box below, put a circle around the one beat notes or rests and put a box around the two beat notes or rests.

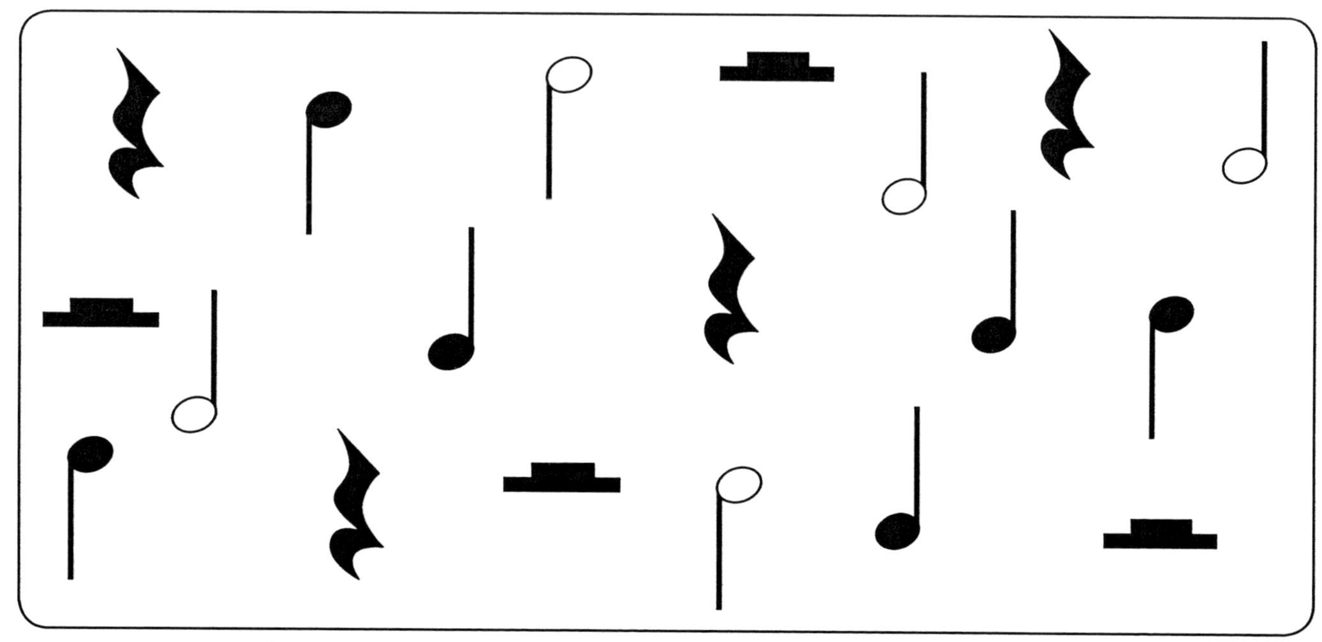

# Sea Song

Add up the notes to get the number needed to color the different parts of the picture.
Add other parts to the fish such as eyes, fins, scales, and mouths.

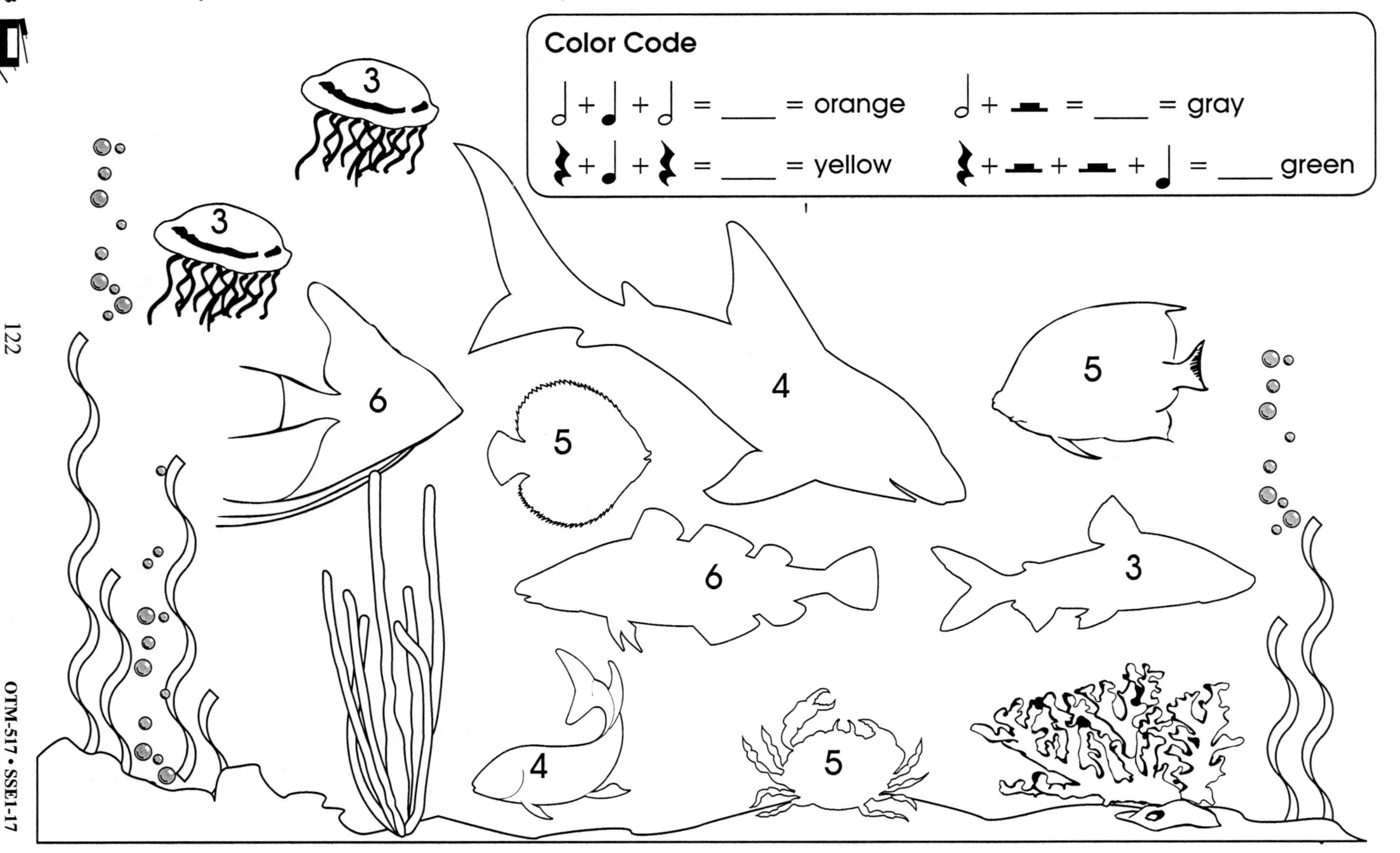


ISBN: 9781554950843

# *Notes to Note*

𝅗𝅥 + ♩ = ________

♩ + 𝄽 + 𝄽 = ________

𝄼 + 𝄽 + 𝅗𝅥 = ________

𝅗𝅥 + 𝄼 + 𝅗𝅥 = ________

♩ + ♩ + 𝄼 = ________

𝅗𝅥 + 𝄽 + ♩ = ________

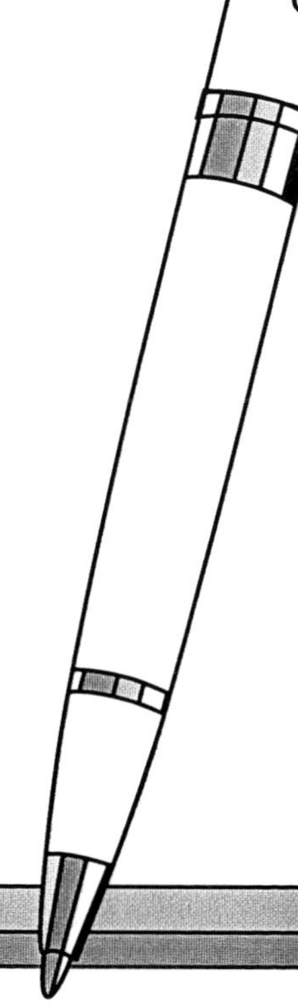

# What Is It?

Color the 2 beat sections blue and the 1 beat sections red.

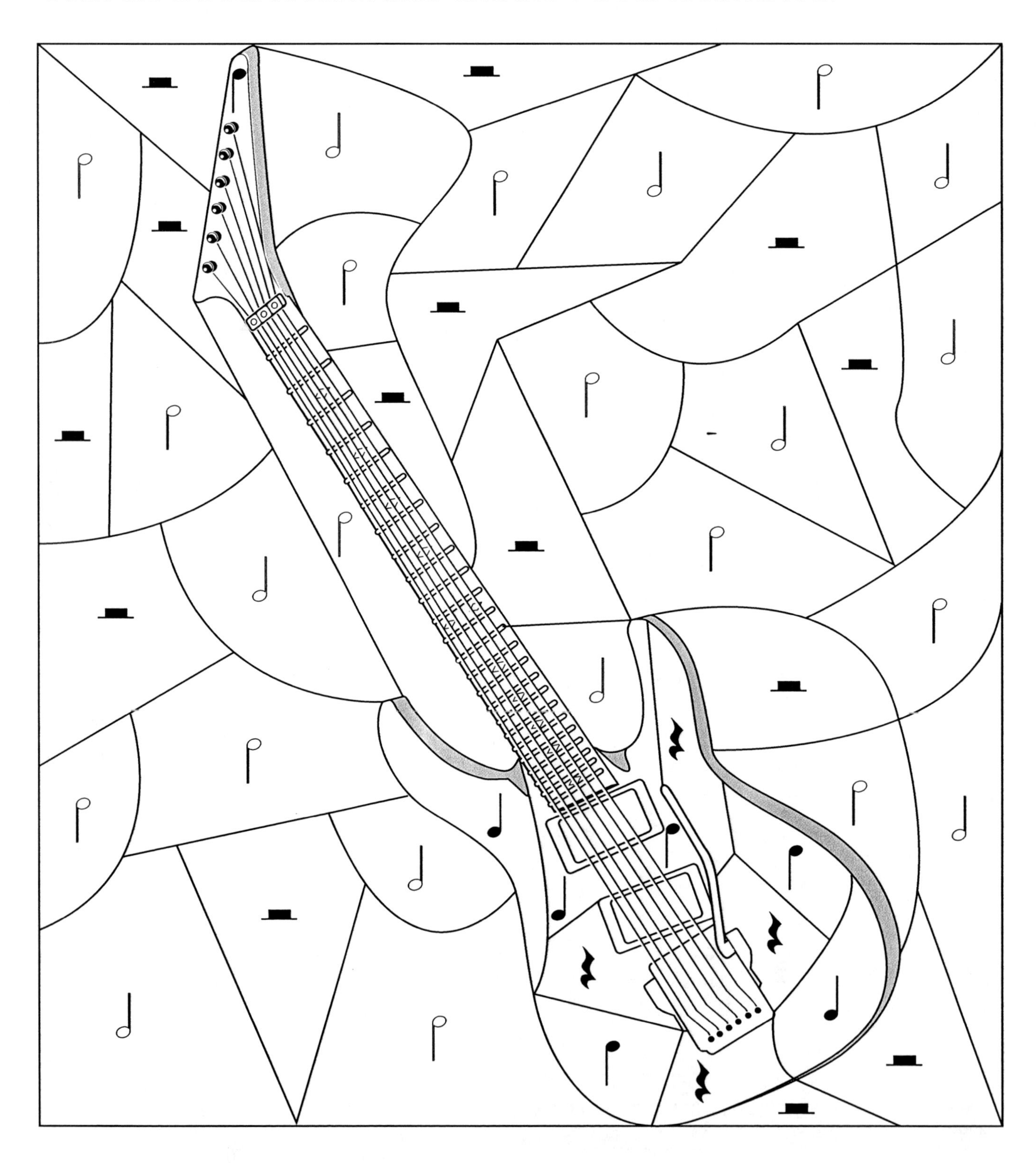

ISBN: 9781554950843

# One, Two, Beats for You

Color all the one beat note and rest sections black and all the two beat note and rest sections red.

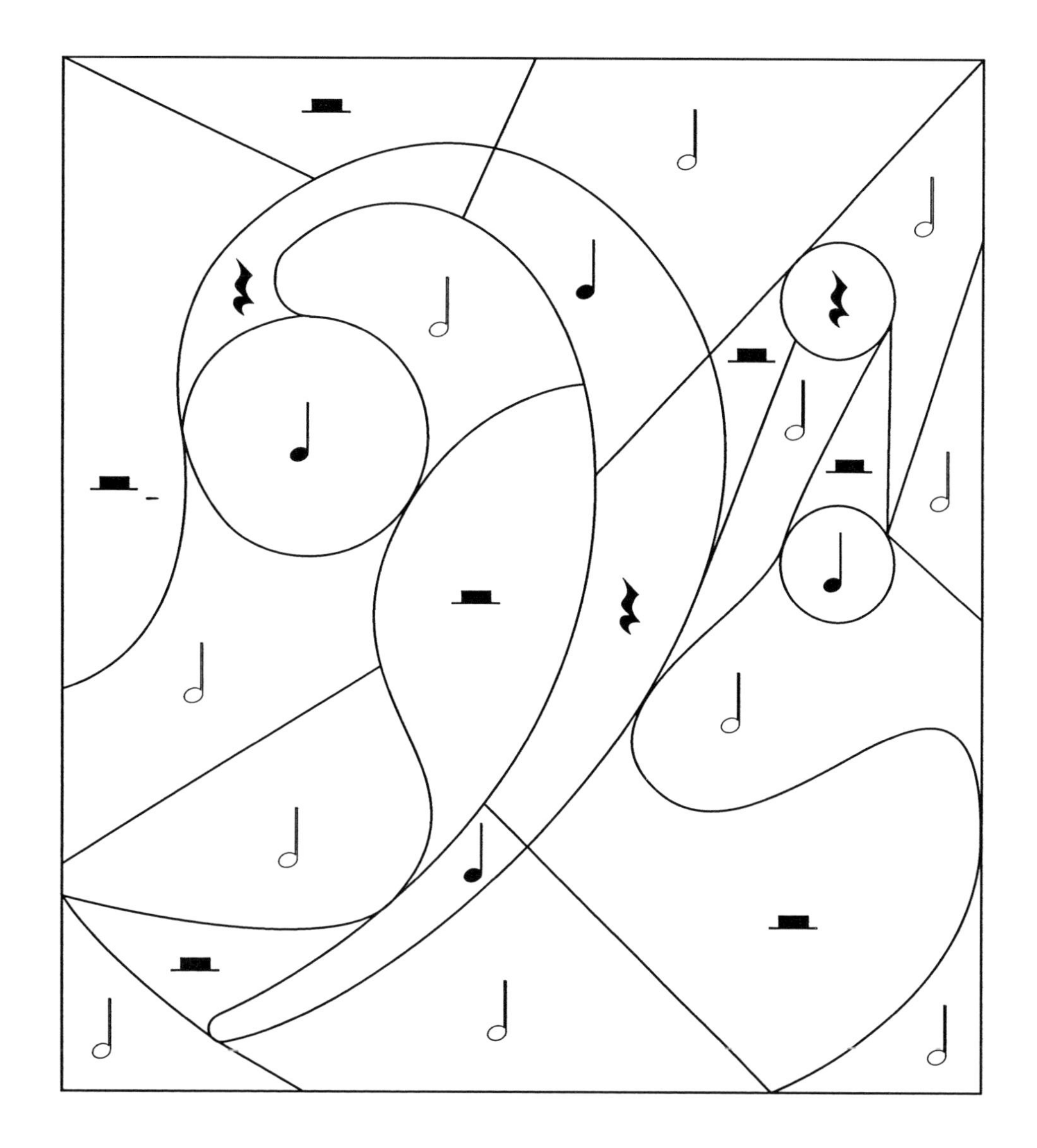

Unscramble the letters to see what the hidden picture is called.

**A S B S L F E C**

It is a ___ ___ ___ ___ ___ ___ ___ ___.

ISBN: 9781554950843

# The Bass Clef and Treble Clef Mystery

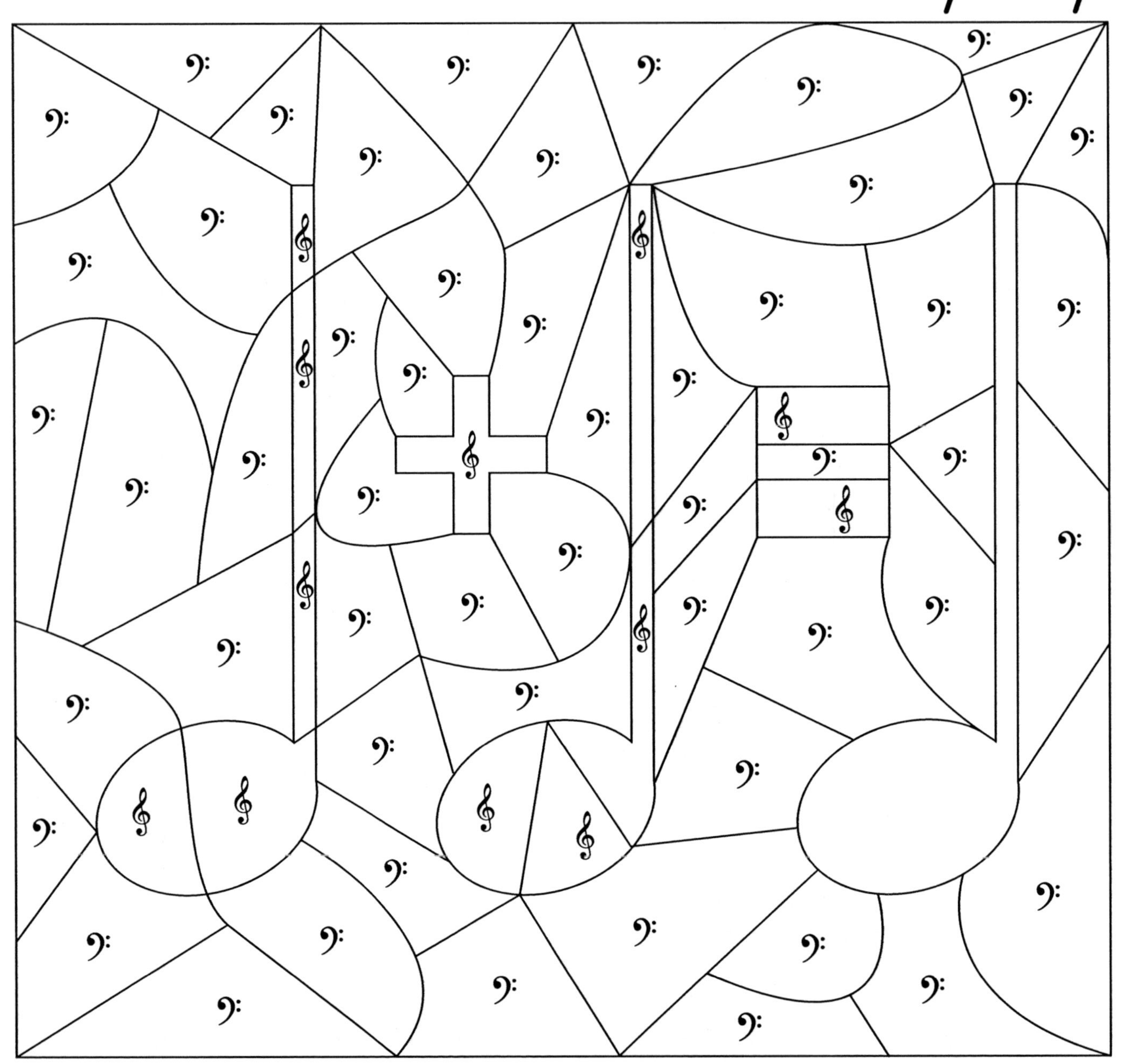

treble clef = black

bass clef = red

# STENCILS

Teacher Notes:

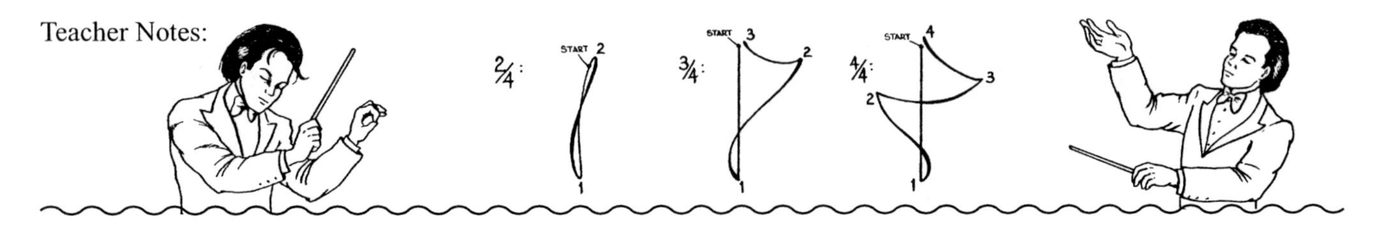


# Musical Elements

This section of the book deals with the following elements:

- The Singing Scale
- The Music Scale
- The Composer

1. If you do not know how to sing the Do (pronounced dough) to do scale with the class and you have a small keyboard or piano, go to the key directly before the group of two black keys. This is C in piano which will be Do. The next white key would be D in piano or Re, and each following white key would be the next note until you end on C again or high Do.

2. On page 129 there is song called Do to Do. When you begin this song begin on C (right before the two black keys). Sing the first whole line on C. Sing the second line on D (this will be the line with Re). Sing the third line on E (Mi) etc. You will end up on high C, which will be high Do. This keeps the song simple and demonstrates how the pitch gets higher on each note.

   The student can color the stairs under the song. This demonstrates the rise in pitch. They could also decorate the page with music notes and other music signs.

3. The worksheets on pages 130 and 131 are to familiarize students with the music scale.

4. The composer Mozart is introduced on pages 132 to 135. This reproducible story booklet can be used to familiarize students with a famous composer and compare themselves to him at the same age. The students are to color the booklet and answer the questions inside. While the children are working on the booklet, play music that Mozart has composed. Mozart wrote many operas and one of them was Eine Kleine Nachtmusik (A Little Night Music) which is done with strings and is very popular. Other suggestions are The Magic Flute, Papagens and Panina's Song.

# Do to Do

Draw a line with an arrow from each step to the line of the song that matches it.

Do is first, it is so low
Re is next, the scale will grow
Mi, Mi, Mi, we tune our voice
Fa is fourth, for a nice choice
Sol is higher than the fourth
La is nice, so sing some more
Ti, hee, hee, it is so high
Do is way up in the sky.

Do Re, Mi, Fa, Sol, La, Ti Do

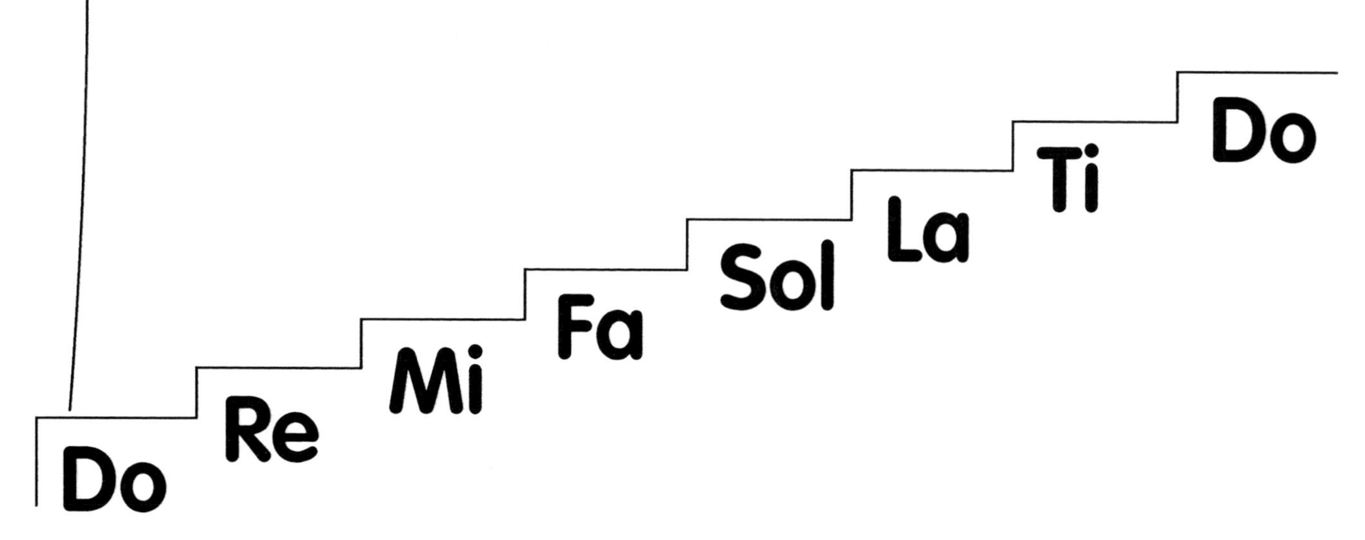


ISBN: 9781554950843

# Musical Words

Fill in the music words with the correct letters.

Use the musical letters in the box below.

A B C D E F OR G

1. ____ ASS

2. BE ____ TS

3. TREBL ____

4. SON ____

5. ____ OUBLE BAR LINE

6. CLE ____

7. PIT ___H

# By the Seashore

Outline all of the pictures and color in the items starting with the musical alphabet - A B C D E F G.

# Mozart and Me

Mozart began to write music when he was four.

What did you like to do when you were four? ______________________

Mozart did not attend school. His father taught him at home.

What things do you like to learn about at school? ____________________

Mozart wrote many operas. In an opera people sing the story. One opera that he wrote was called the "Magic Flute."

Do you enjoy singing? ____________

Mozart liked to dress up. He had many different velvet coats.

Do you have a favorite costume or outfit? ______________________

Mozart wrote so much music that it added up to 202 hours.

Do you like to write stories or music? ______________________

Mozart loved animals and owned a dog.

Do you own a pet? ____________________

During one of his concerts, Mozart tried to catch a cat walking across the stage.

Have you done anything funny? ________________________________

Teacher Notes:

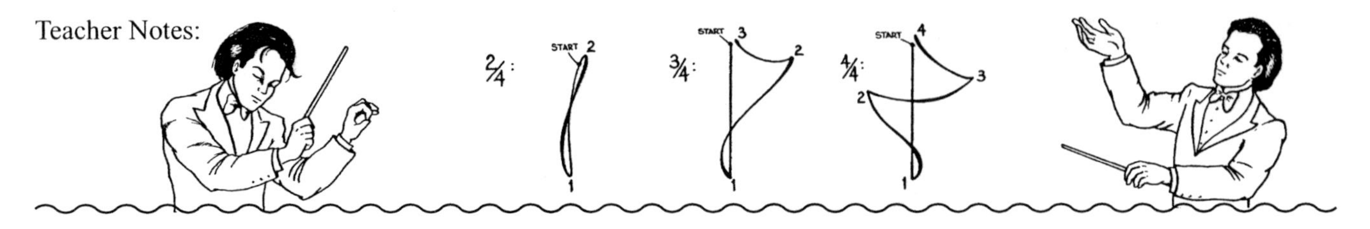


# String Instruments

The following activities are to be used as follow-ups to lessons on string instruments.

- The story of the string instrument characters will introduce the students to the instruments. These pages may be made into a story booklet for each student to read and color or they may be part of the music booklet or glued into student scrapbooks.

- The teacher may also bring string instruments to the classroom and demonstrate how they are played. Try to obtain these instruments from a local secondary school and have the students from a school band demonstrate playing them. If a student in the classroom has any of the stringed instruments at home, encourage them to bring them to school. A parent who plays one of the instruments could be approached and invited to play for the class.

- The tissue box harp that is to be made will bring added enjoyment and fun for the students during this section. See page 140 for the teacher instructions.

- The worksheets on pages 141, 142, 143, and 144 will remind students of important facts in music. Barney Bass and Hanna Harp will aid in the learning of bar lines. Verna Viola is helping with the knowledge of the double bar line and the musical alphabet. Charlie Cello is demonstrating the one and two beat notes. Make sure the student knows to connect any dotted sections which act as an aid.

- The dot to dot of the violin has two number ones. Make sure the students are aware of this.

- Creativity and enjoyment are the most important keys in music advancement.

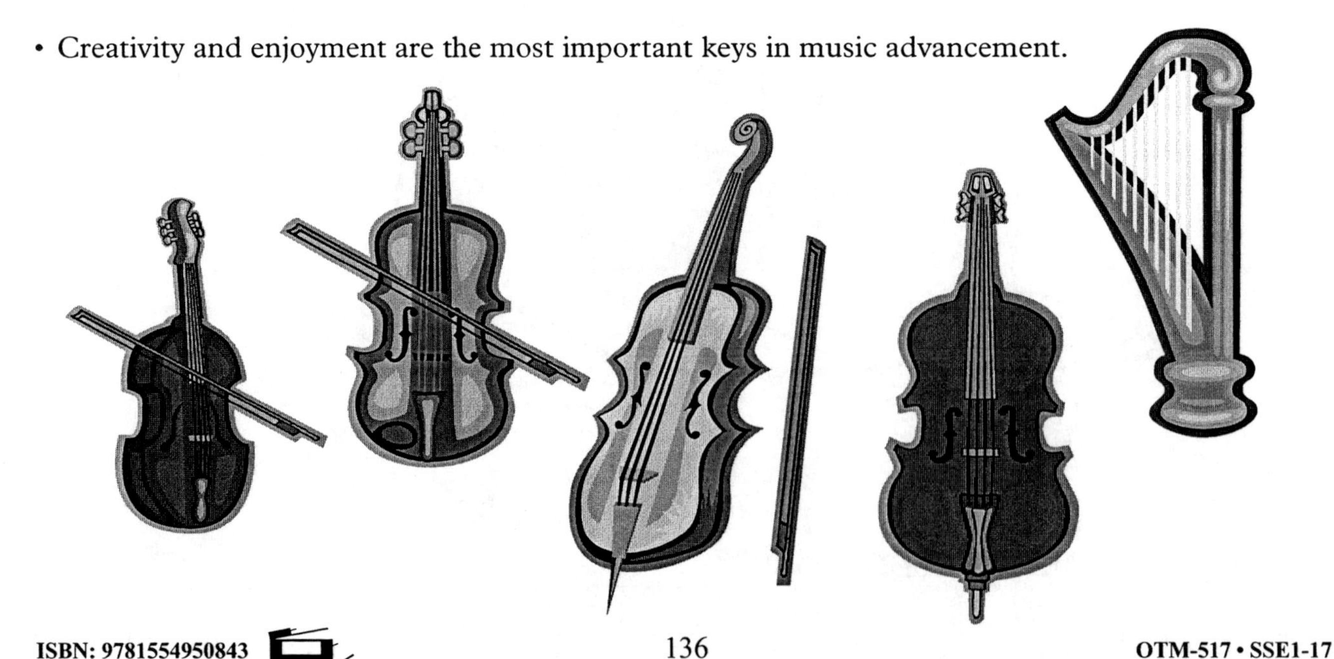

# The Big Concert

It was the night of the big concert and Vicky Violin was so scared. It was the first time she had a solo. This meant she would be playing all alone. She arrived at the concert hall early.

Verna Viola and Hannah Harp were practicing their duet. A duet is when two instruments play together. They played so beautifully. The harp was soft and pretty and the viola was deeper and sweet.

The concert began and Barney Bass introduced everyone with his low and booming voice.

Vicky Violin was the last to play. She tried to make a sound but was terrified. All that came out was a screech. The audience held their breath.

Vicky then remembered to think happy thoughts and remembered building sand castles on the beach with Hannah Harp.

Then it happened. She began to play the most exciting solo of the night. The audience clapped their hands and stamped their feet. Vicky was so happy. From then on, she loved to play solos.

# The Tissue Box Harp

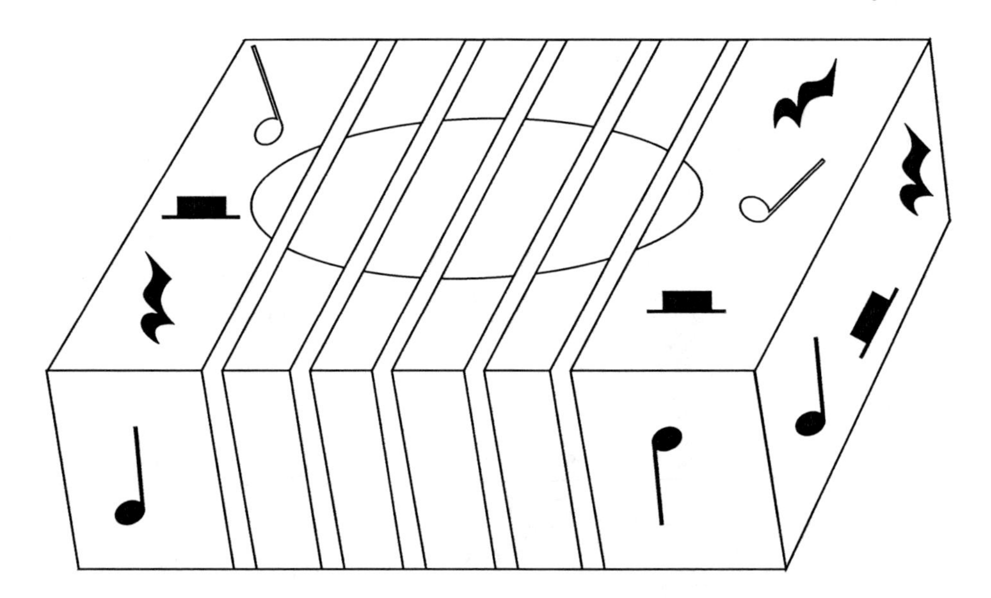

## Teacher Instructions

### List of Material Needed:

- an empty tissue box for each student
- supplies used for decorations such as colored paper, stickers, wallpaper, crayons, paint, sparkles, etc.
- glue
- different sized rubber bands with different thicknesses
- staples and a stapler

### Instructions:

1. Decorate the tissue box with the materials that you have chosen.

2. Stretch at least five rubber bands the short way around the box. They should end up over top of the hole with the thinnest starting at one side and the thickest at the other side. The bands should be stapled in place. You are ready to pluck the strings and make beautiful music.

# Barney Bass and the Monkey Bars

Connect the dots and finish the picture.

Bar Lines

# Hanna's Party

Hanna Harp is having a party.

For Pin the Tail on the Donkey, she is going to stop the music 1/4 of the way through the first time.

Draw an arrow 1/4 of the way through for the first time. Join the dots.

Then draw an arrow for the second time.

This will be 1/2 of the way through.

The music is separated by bar lines into four parts.

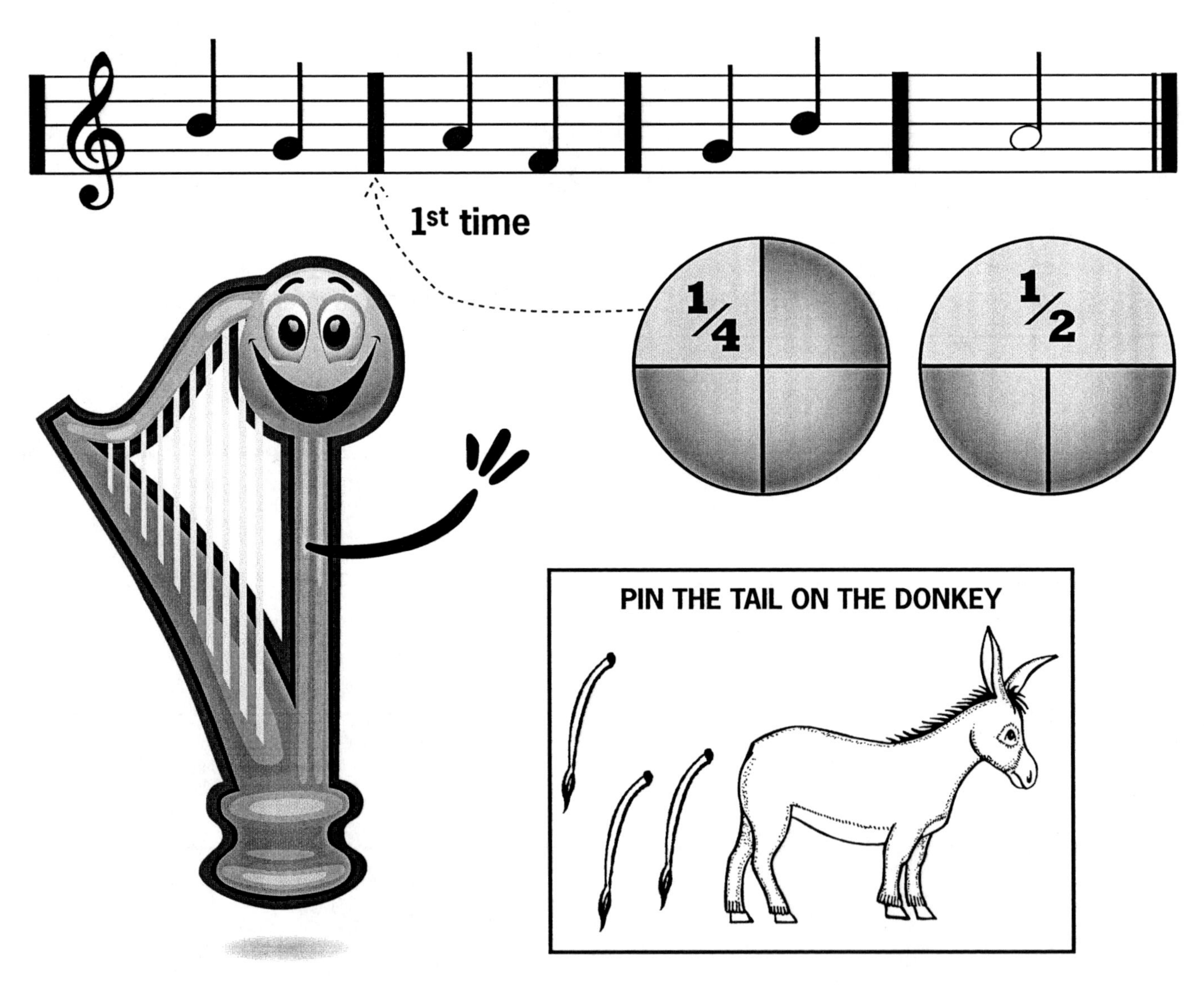

# Color with Verna

Using A B C D E F and G as a guide, circle all the letters of the music alphabet below.

Join the dots for an example.

Color the circled letters blue.

Color the other letters any color you wish.

This will help Verna learn her music alphabet.

# Charlie's March

Charlie Cello is going in the music parade for the last day of school.

He is holding the 2-beat note.

His job is to say 1,2 over and over again while he is walking in the parade.

Color Charlie Cello and the numbers 1 and 2 but leave the 2-beat note white.

Fill in the blanks under the bars of music and count or tap out the last line.

1, 2

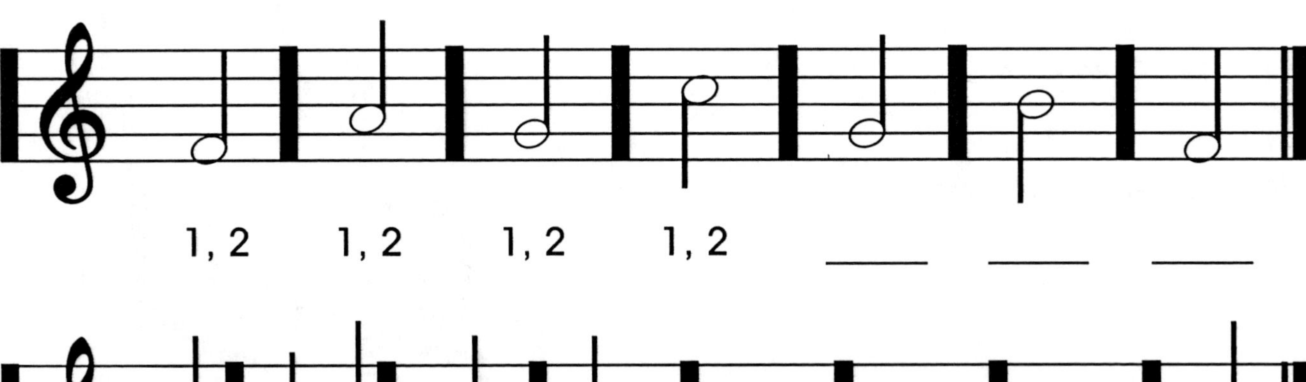


1, 2 1, 2 1, 2 1, 2 1, 2 1, 2 1, 2 1, 2

ISBN: 9781554950843 

# How Do I Make Music?

Connect the dotted numbers to find the musical instrument.

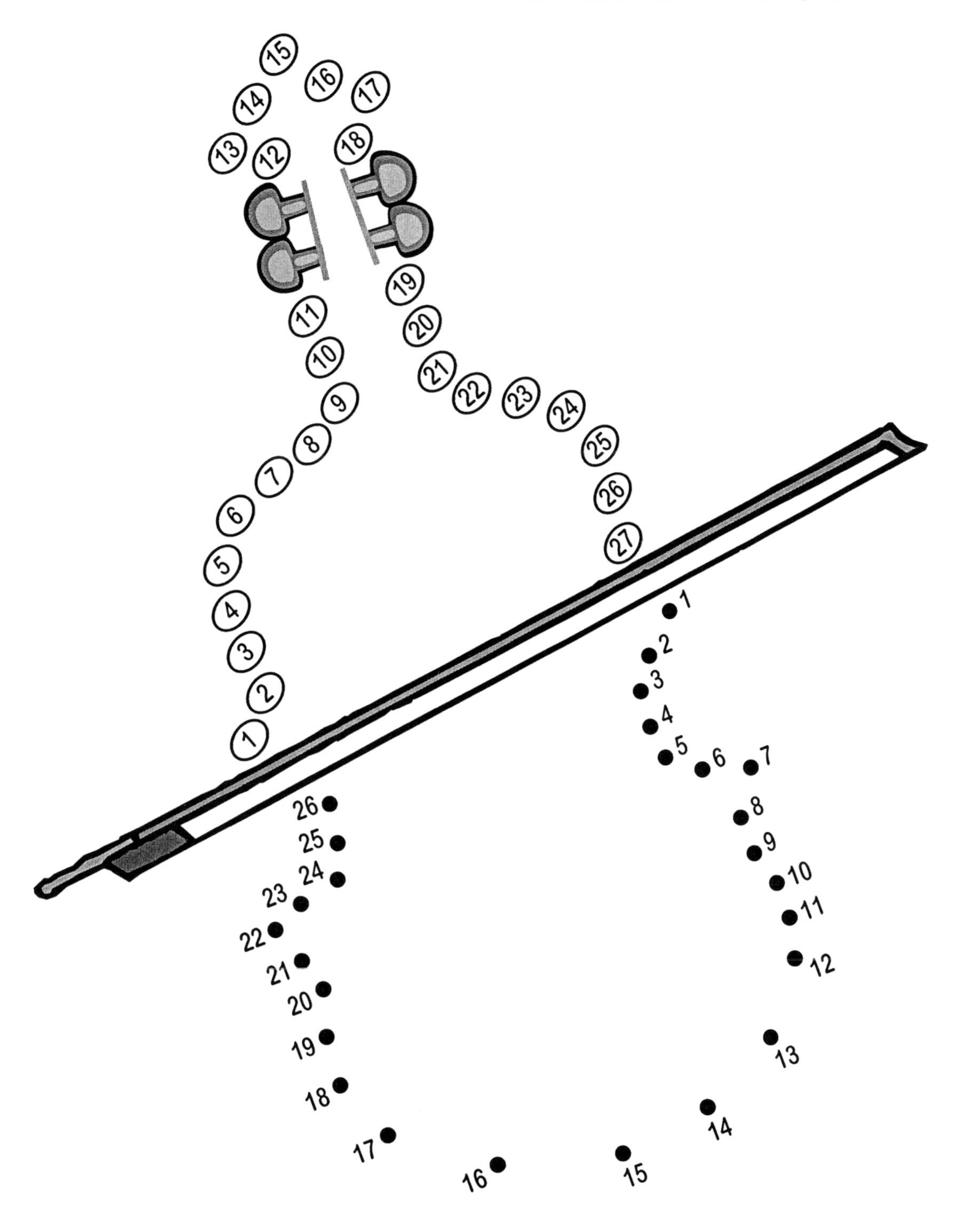

I am called a ______________________ .

ISBN: 9781554950843

Teacher Notes:

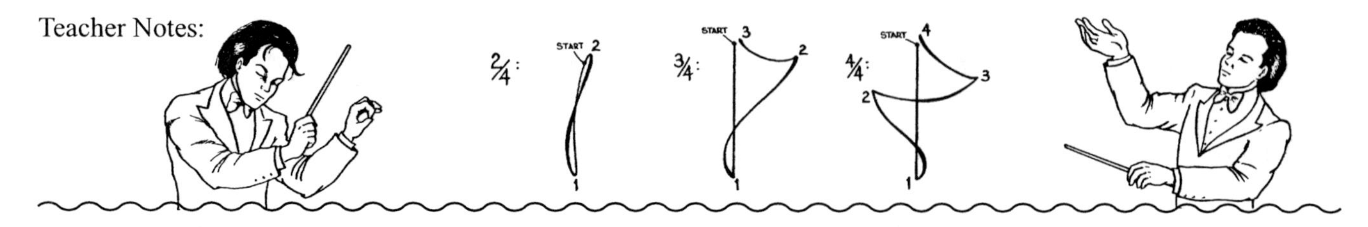


# Holiday Worksheets

The holiday worksheets found on pages 147 to 153 contain activities that have been designed to review musical facts previously taught. These worksheets will be fun and exciting for the students to complete. Their imaginations should run free and their creativity soar.

- The Christmas tree is to be decorated using the music signs that are on the tree stand.
- The Heart to Heart should be colored and cut out. This can be made into a Valentine
- My Musical Valentine is a word search but before the search begins, the heart must be finished with a solid line connecting all the same music signs.
- The Lucky Rainbow should be colored after adding up the notes and rests and using the code.
- The Double Surprise should be colored according to the code.
- Sing into Spring is a picture with three eggs that need decorating.
- Fish Beats is to be colored according to the code. See how many fish each boy will catch.

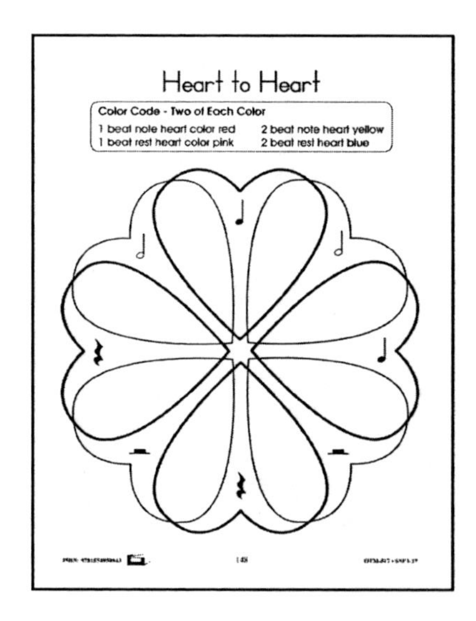

Heart to Heart

Color Code - Two of Each Color

1 beat note heart color red 2 beat note heart yellow

1 beat rest heart color pink 2 beat rest heart blue

The Lucky Rainbow

Color the rainbow after adding up the beats. Use the codes on the shamrocks. Also color the hat and pot of gold according to the code.

Fish Beats

Color the little boy's rod yellow and all the one beat fish yellow.

Color the big boy's rod orange and all the two beat fish orange.

Each boy catches fish that match the color of their rods.

How many fish did each boy catch?

The little boy caught __ fish. The big boy caught __ fish.

# The Music Tree

Decorate the tree with notes, rests, and symbols and then color.

ISBN: 9781554950843

# Heart to Heart

**Color Code - Two of Each Color**

1 beat note heart color red
1 beat rest heart color pink
2 beat note heart yellow
2 beat rest heart blue

ISBN: 9781554950843

# My Musical Valentine

Connect the music symbols with a solid line.

Circle these words in the valentine. bar line one beat two beats note rest treble bass

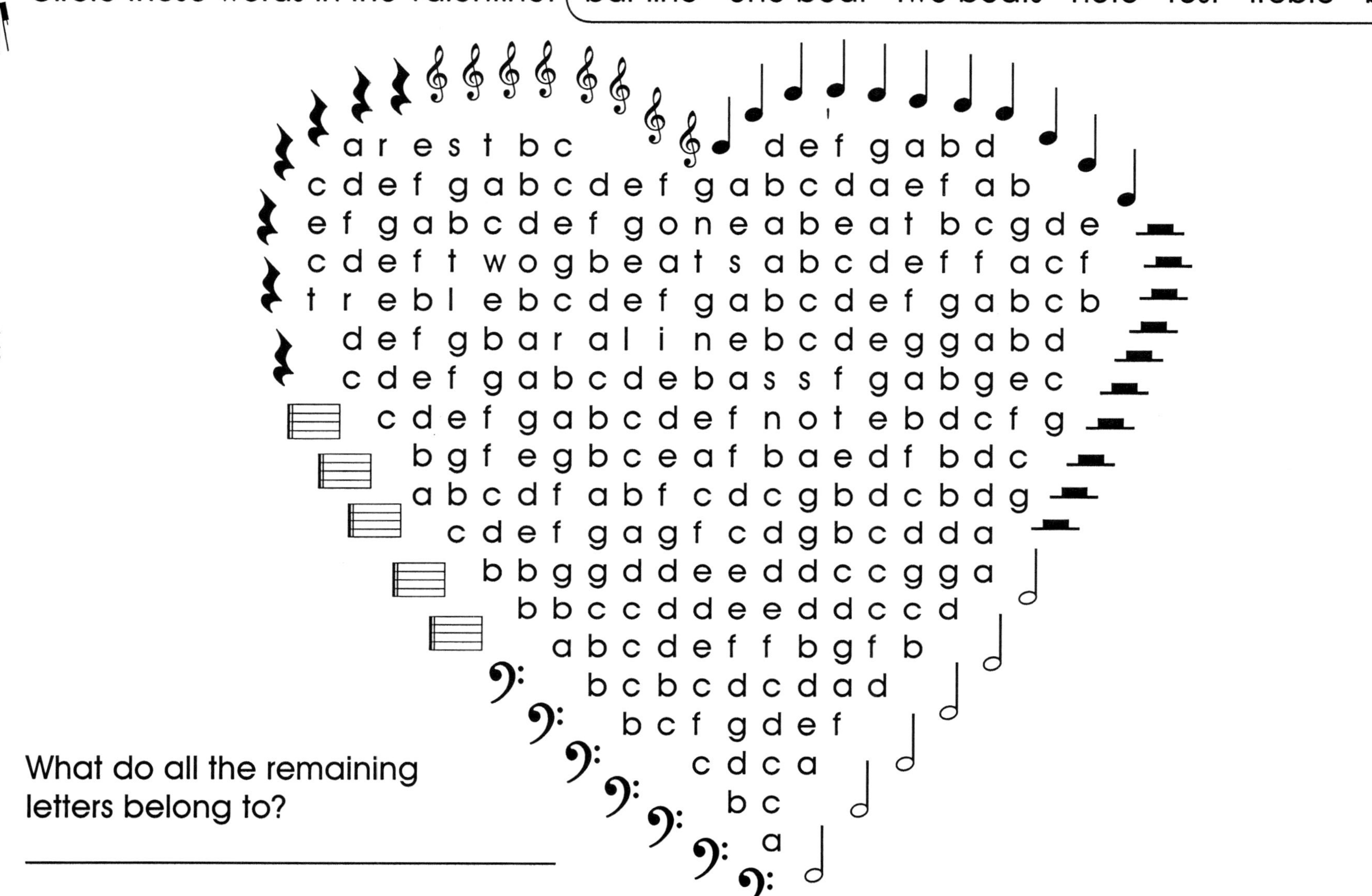


What do all the remaining letters belong to?

___________________________

# The Lucky Rainbow

Color the rainbow after adding up the beats. Use the codes on the shamrocks. Also color the hat and pot of gold according to the code.

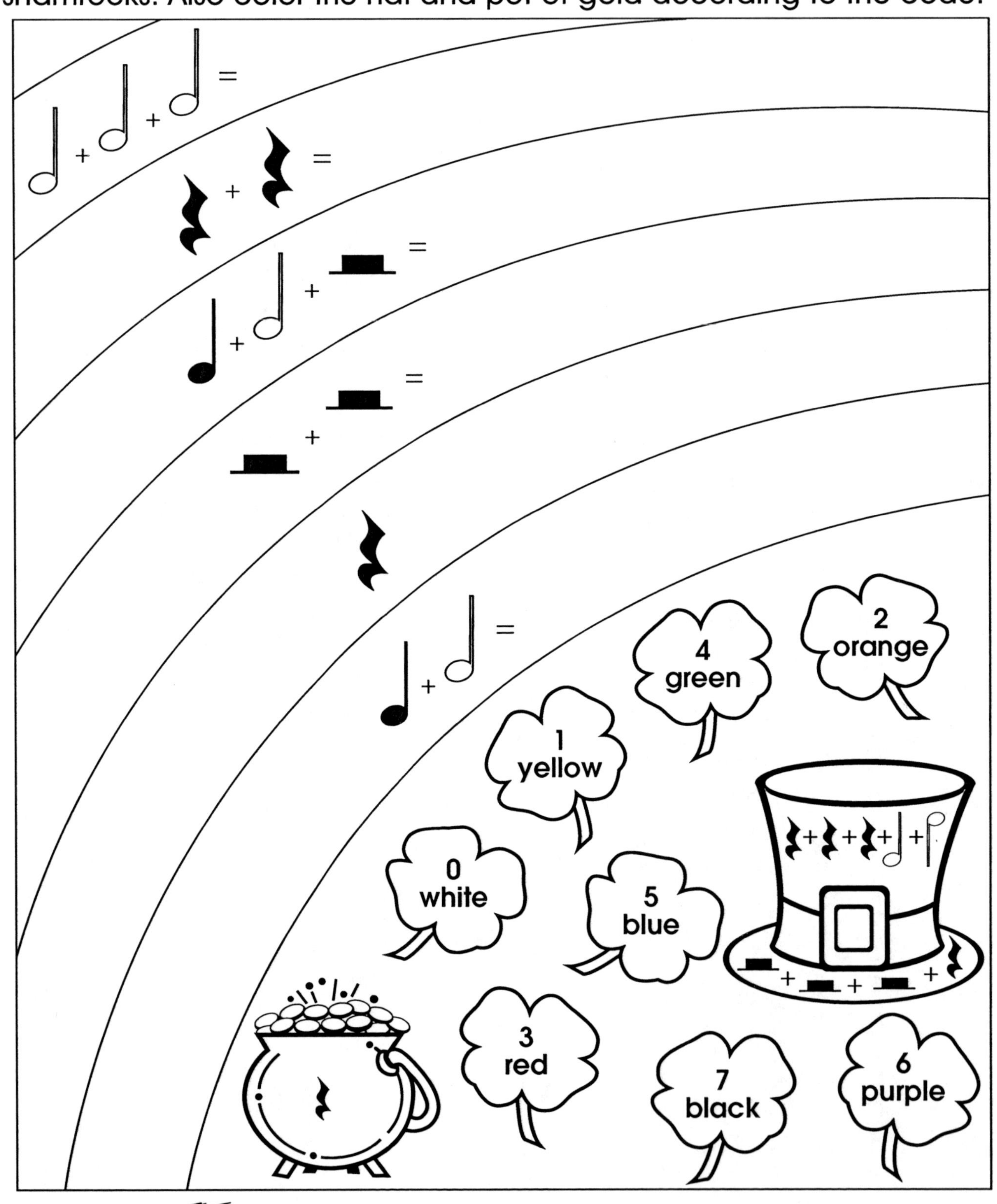


ISBN: 9781554950843

# The Double Surprise

Color the one beat sections green. Color the two beat sections blue.

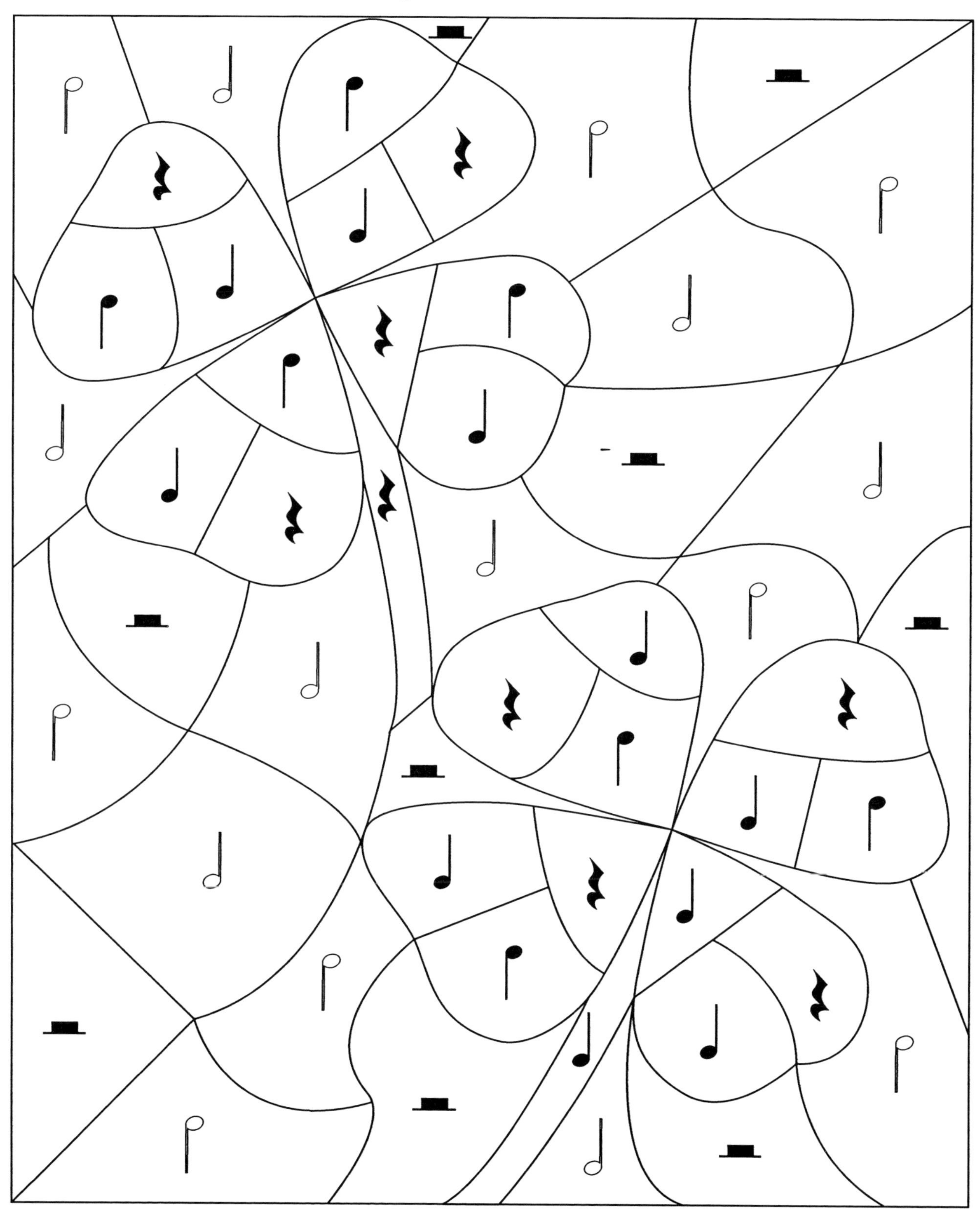

# Sing into Spring

Decorate the eggs with

two beat notes

two beat rests

bass clef

bar lines

Color the rest of the picture.

# Fish Beats

Color the little boy's rod yellow and all the one beat fish yellow.

Color the big boy's rod orange and all the two beat fish orange.

Each boy catches fish that match the color of their rods.

How many fish did each boy catch?

The little boy caught ___ fish. The big boy caught ___ fish.

# Musical Games

## Game #1 - Spinner Quest

**Game Pieces:**
a spinner, the question and answer sheet, somewhere to score

**Preparations:**

1. The spinner needs to be assembled before playing. It is found on page 156.
2. This page with the large circle numbered 1 to 14 must be cut out and glued onto the pie plate.
3. The spinner, which can be made from plastic, needs to be attached with a duo tang clip in the center. This spinner, which is shaped like an arrow, should be able to spin and point to the numbers which coincide with the question sheet.
4. Score cards are needed, or the score can be kept on the chalkboard.

**Playing the Game:**

1. This game can be played as a class or split into groups.
2. The first student spins.
3. The teacher then reads the corresponding question.
4. The group or individual must answer correctly for one point.
5. Individually, players are eliminated with a wrong answer. As a group, teams must reach a certain number of points to win.

## Game #2 - Musical Memory

1. This is a memory card game.
2. Pages 159 and 160 need to be photocopied, mounted on a sturdy backing, and cut to assemble the cards for the game.
3. The cards are then lined up face down in any order and player one turns over two random cards to try and match a pair.
4. If they don't match, the cards are returned face down and the next player takes a turn.
5. If a pair is matched, the pair is kept and the player takes an additional turn until he/she can not match a pair.
6. The player with the most pairs wins the game.
7. Do not include the old composer card for this game.

# Musical Games

## Game #3 - The Old Composer

1. The same cards, as in Game #2, are used for this game, including the Old Composer card.
2. Players are dealt all the cards.
3. Player #1 asks the player on the left for a card that he/she has in his/her hand and tries to get a matching pair. If the player does, the player goes again. If the player doesn't, the next player plays.
4. The pairs of cards are displayed in front of them and counted at the end.
5. The player with the most pairs wins the game.
6. The player left with the old composer card becomes "The Old Composer."
7. Make sure if you are adding additional copies of the cards that you have only one old composer card so there isn't a matching pair.

## Game #4 - Go Rest

1. This is also a card game, using the cards with the rests.
2. They also need to be assembled.
3. The object of the game is to get four of the same cards for a set which gives one point.
4. Four copies of page 161 are needed for a full deck of cards.
5. Players are dealt seven cards.
6. The rest of the cards are put in the middle face down, in a pile.
7. The first player asks the player on the left for a certain card. The player must give all of the cards in his/her hand that add up to the number of rests asked for.
8. If the player is successful, he/she can ask for a different one until the player asked doesn't have that card and says "Go Rest."
9. Player one takes a card from the middle and it is player two's turn.
10. When four of the same cards are collected, the set is placed down in front of the player.
11. The highest number of sets wins the game.

## Suggestions

1. The games will teach the students to recognize music signs, instruments, and the value of rests.
2. You may want extra sets of cards because they tend to wear out after time. If the students are having problems recognizing the signs, you could also color code the same cards to make it easier.
3. If you are working in groups, you may want to have other materials such as reproducibles and worksheets available in case some games take longer than others to play.

ISBN: 9781554950843  

## Spinner

GAME #1

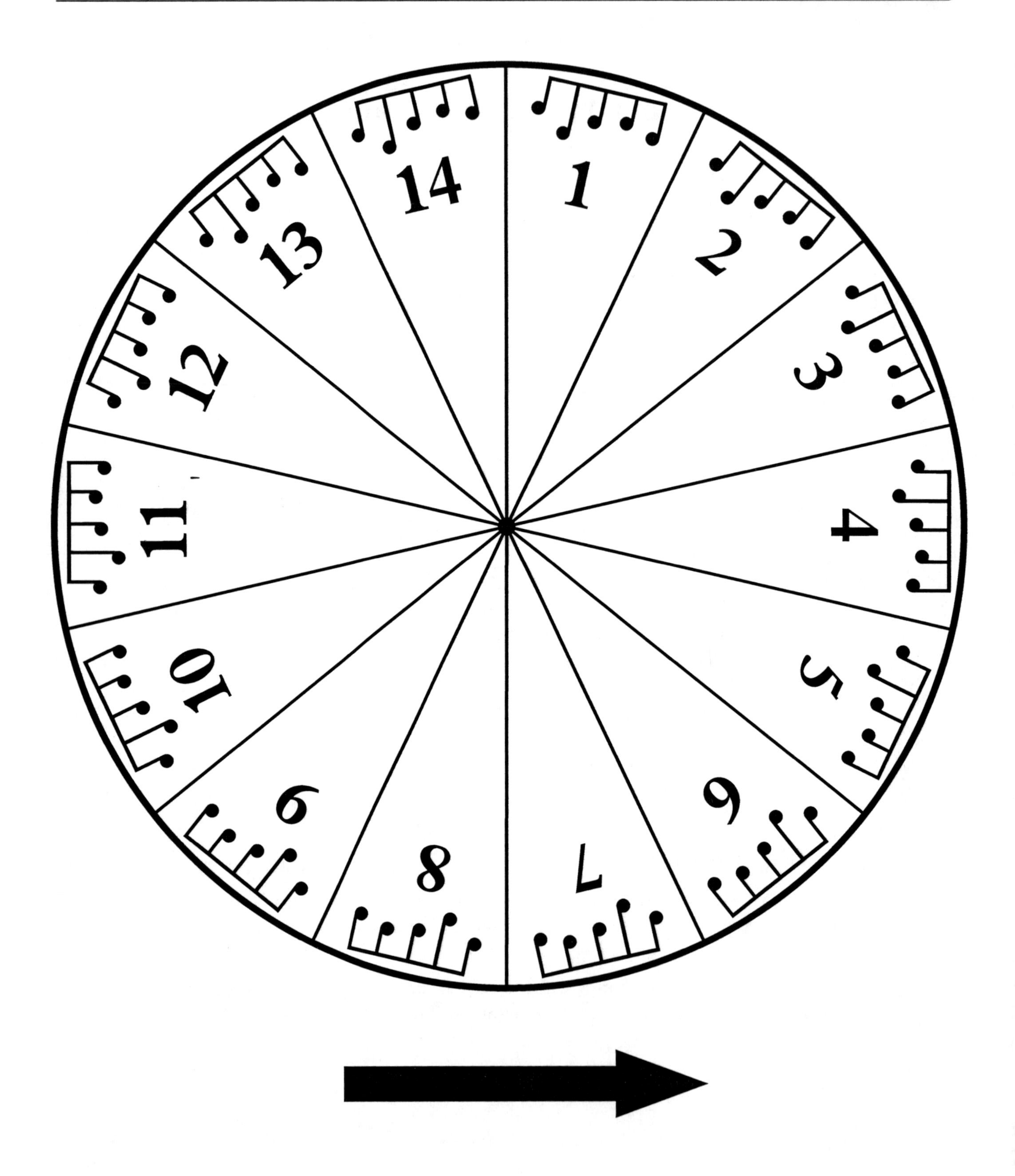


ISBN: 9781554950843

# Spinner Quest

GAME #1

## Questions and Answers: Group A

1. The soft sounding instrument that has many strings and has pedals to make the sounds higher or lower is called a ______________. (harp)
2. The small string instrument that is played with a bow is called a __________. (violin)
3. The deep low-sounding large string instrument that you have to stand up to play is called a __________. (bass)
4. The medium sized string instrument that leans on the floor, but you sit down to play it, is called a __________. (cello)
5. The clef that is for low notes is called the __________. (bass Clef)
6. What pet did Mozart have when he was a boy? (a dog)
7. Who taught Mozart his schoolwork? (his father)
8. How many hours did Mozart's songs add up to? (202 hours)
9. What divides music into sections? (bar lines)
10. How many beats does the rest that looks like a hat receive? (2 beats)
11. How many beats does the white note get? (2 beats)
12. What do you play a viola with? (a bow)
13. Is a bass larger or smaller that a violin? (larger)
14. Which is smaller, a quarter or a half of something? (a quarter)

# Spinner Quest

GAME #1

### Questions and Answers: Group B

1. What color is a one beat note? (black)
2. What clef is used for high notes? (the treble clef)
3. What comes after do in the singing scale? (re)
4. How many beats does a squiggly rest get? (one)
5. What letters are used in music? (A B C D E F G)
6. Where do you find a double bar line? (at the end of a song)
7. Is a viola larger or smaller than a violin? (larger)
8. Is a bass higher or lower sounding than a viola? (lower)
9. How many lines are on a staff? (five)
10. How many spaces are there on a staff? (four)
11. What comes after la in the singing scale? (ti)
12. How many beats would tick, tock be? (two)
13. What colors are the keys on a keyboard? (black and white)
14. The black keys on a keyboard come in groups of __________ (two) or groups of __________. (three)

# Cards

GAMES #2 & #3

ISBN: 9781554950843

# Cards

GAMES #2 & #3

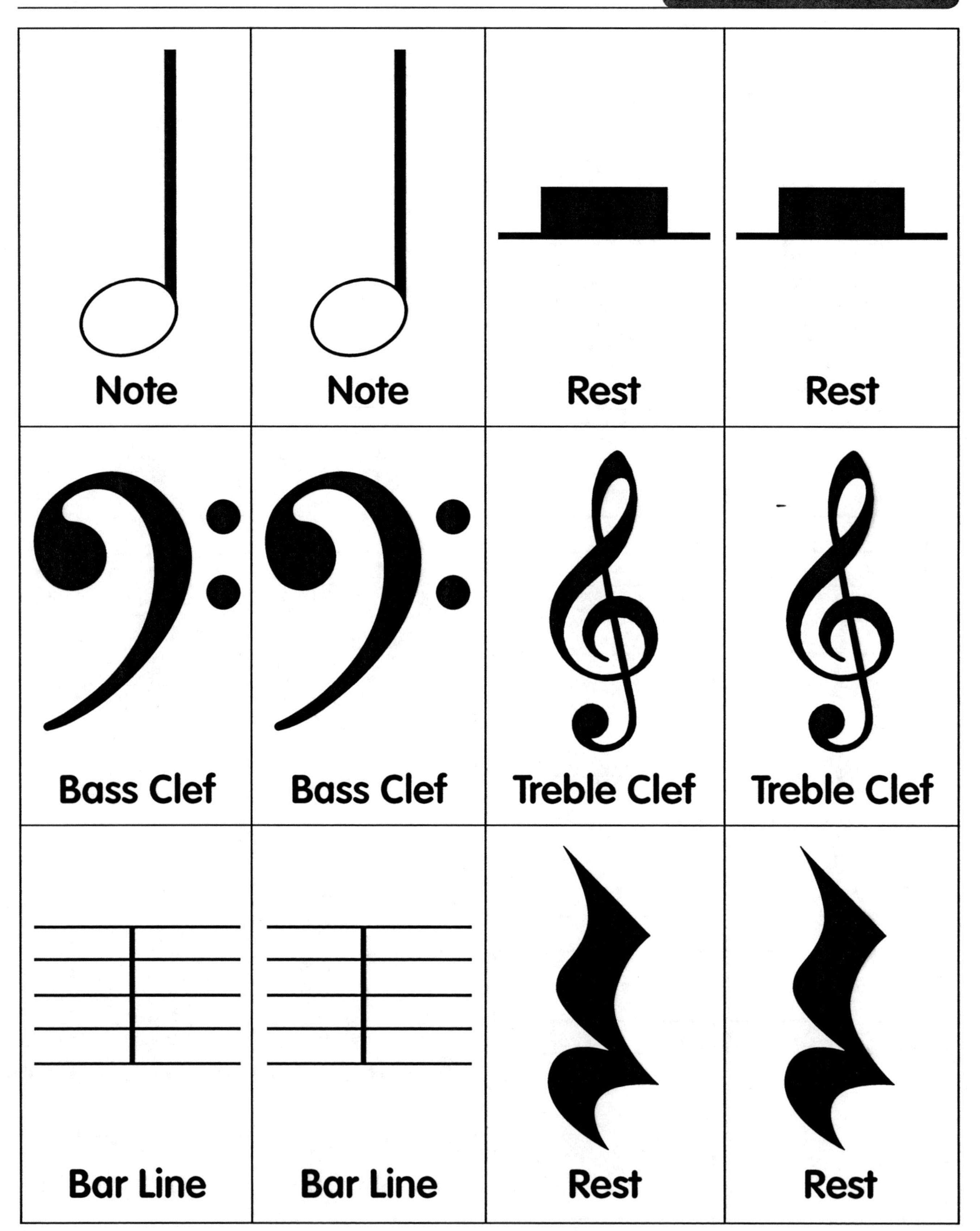

# Go Rest! Grade 2 Cards

GAME #4

Teacher Notes:

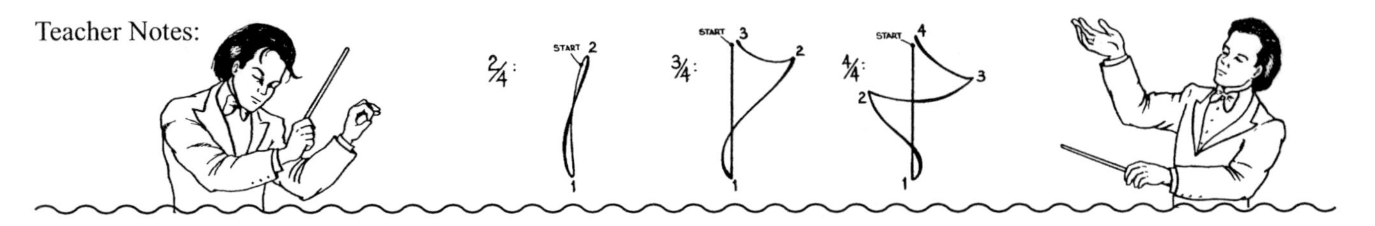


# Review Worksheets, Quiz, and Review Art

1. There are two pages of review facts which will help the student review the signs learned before writing the Quiz. The two pages should be colored according to the code on the page. The music sign, the arrow, and the term should end up all being the same color.

2. The Quiz can be used as a test. The arrows are used so that the lines do not cross one another and you end up not knowing which line goes with the sign. You can also use a different color for each sign. The arrows would then not be necessary. The Quiz is out of 10, so the first answer is an example and they would get one right as a bonus.

3. The art work will enable the students to be creative and to think about the information that they have learned in this book. It might even interest them enough to want to learn to play an instrument. The art pages will help bring the information to the outside world.

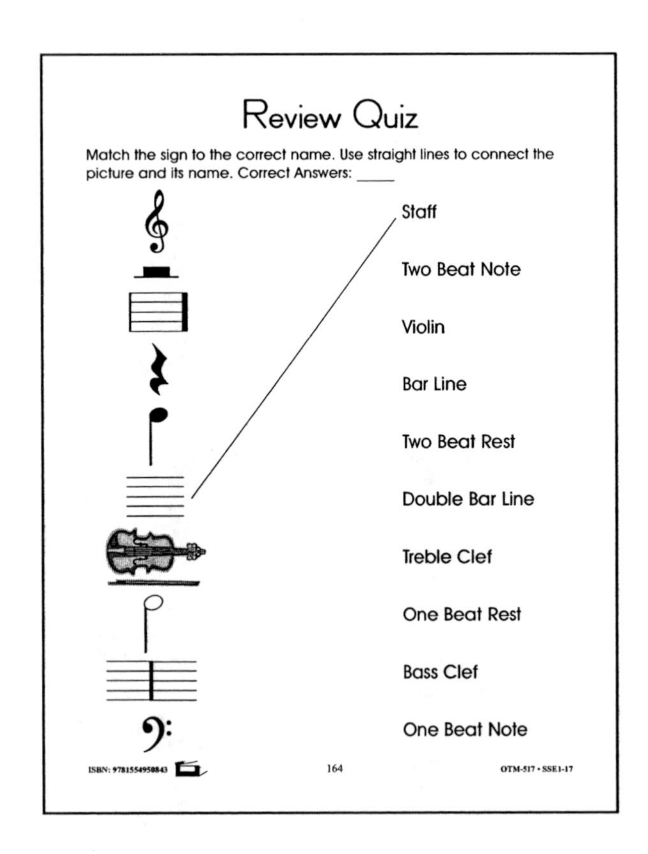

Review Quiz

Match the sign to the correct name. Use straight lines to connect the picture and its name. Correct Answers: ____

Staff
Two Beat Note
Violin
Bar Line
Two Beat Rest
Double Bar Line
Treble Clef
One Beat Rest
Bass Clef
One Beat Note

ISBN: 9781554950843 164 OTM-517 • SSE1-17

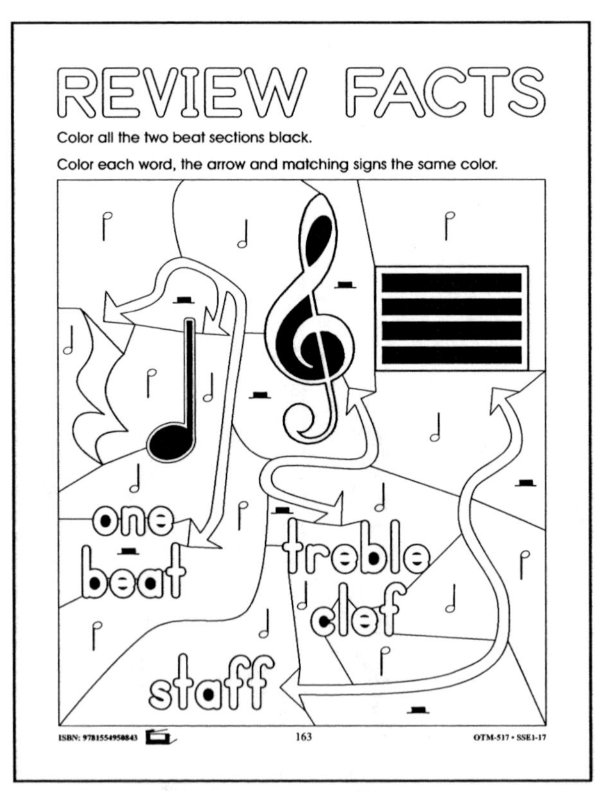

REVIEW FACTS

Color all the two beat sections black.

Color each word, the arrow and matching signs the same color.



ISBN: 9781554950843 163 OTM-517 • SSE1-17

# REVIEW FACTS

Color all the two beat sections black.

Color each word, the arrow, and the matching signs the same color.

# Review Quiz

Match the sign to the correct name. Use straight lines to connect the picture and its name. Correct Answers: _____

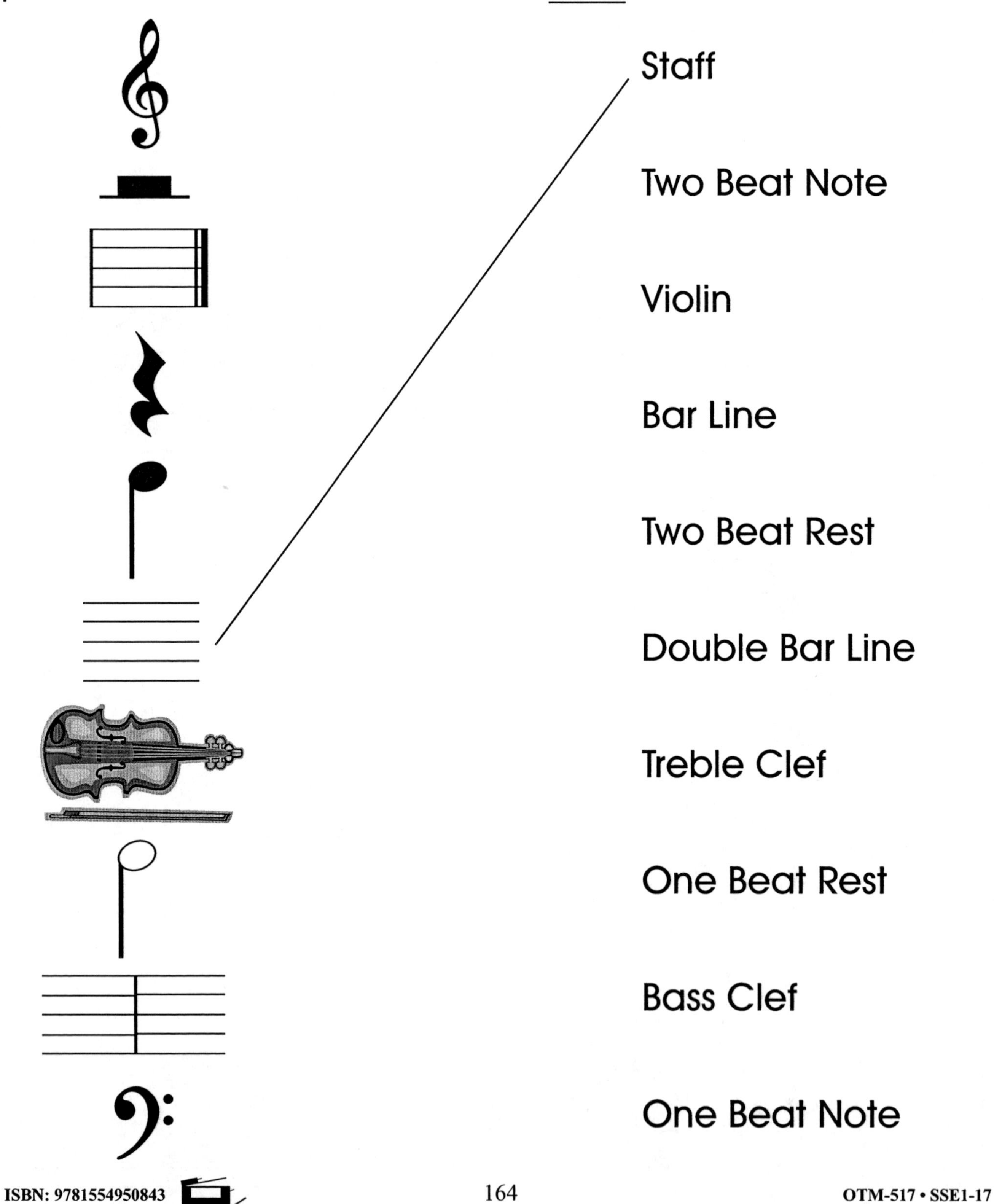

# A Musical Instrument

Draw a picture of your favorite musical instrument that you learned about in the box below. On the lines provided, print a few sentences about the one that you chose.

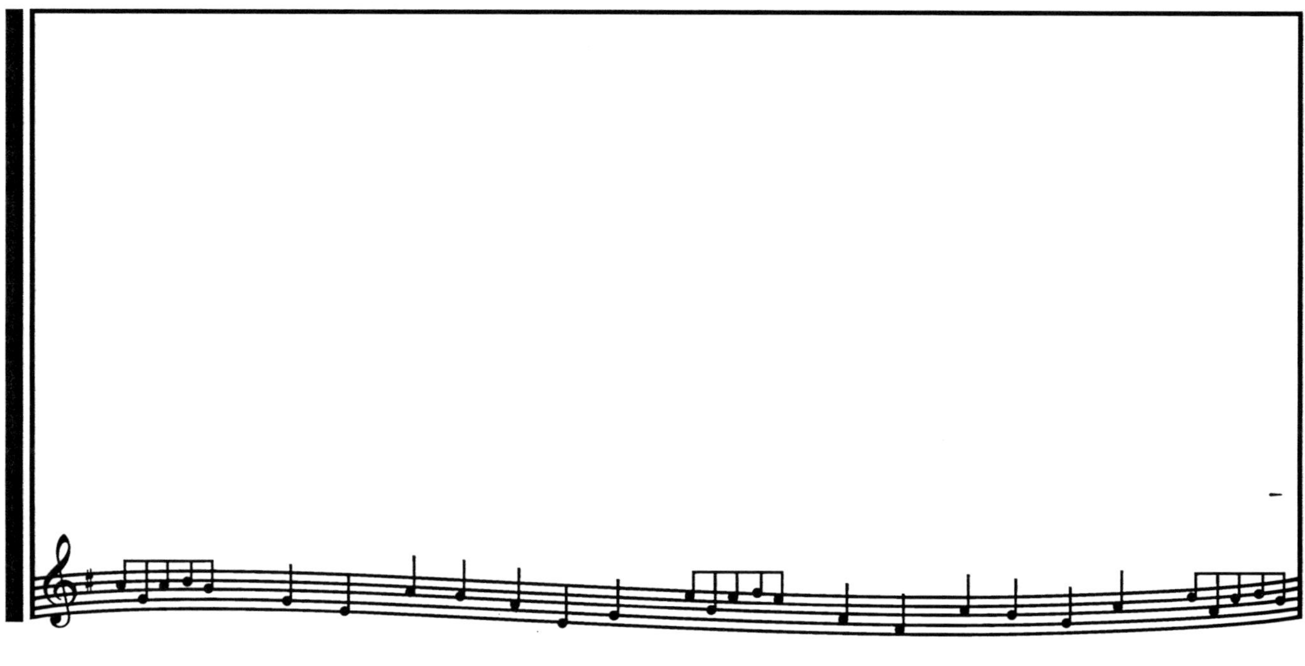

Draw a picture of you playing the instrument that you liked learning about the best.

# Music In My World

I heard music playing ______________________________________

I saw ______________________________________ playing music.

It was ______________________________________

Draw a picture of one of the sentences in the box below.

# Fun With Musical Signs

Draw two musical signs that you learned about and make them into something.

Put each one in a box below.

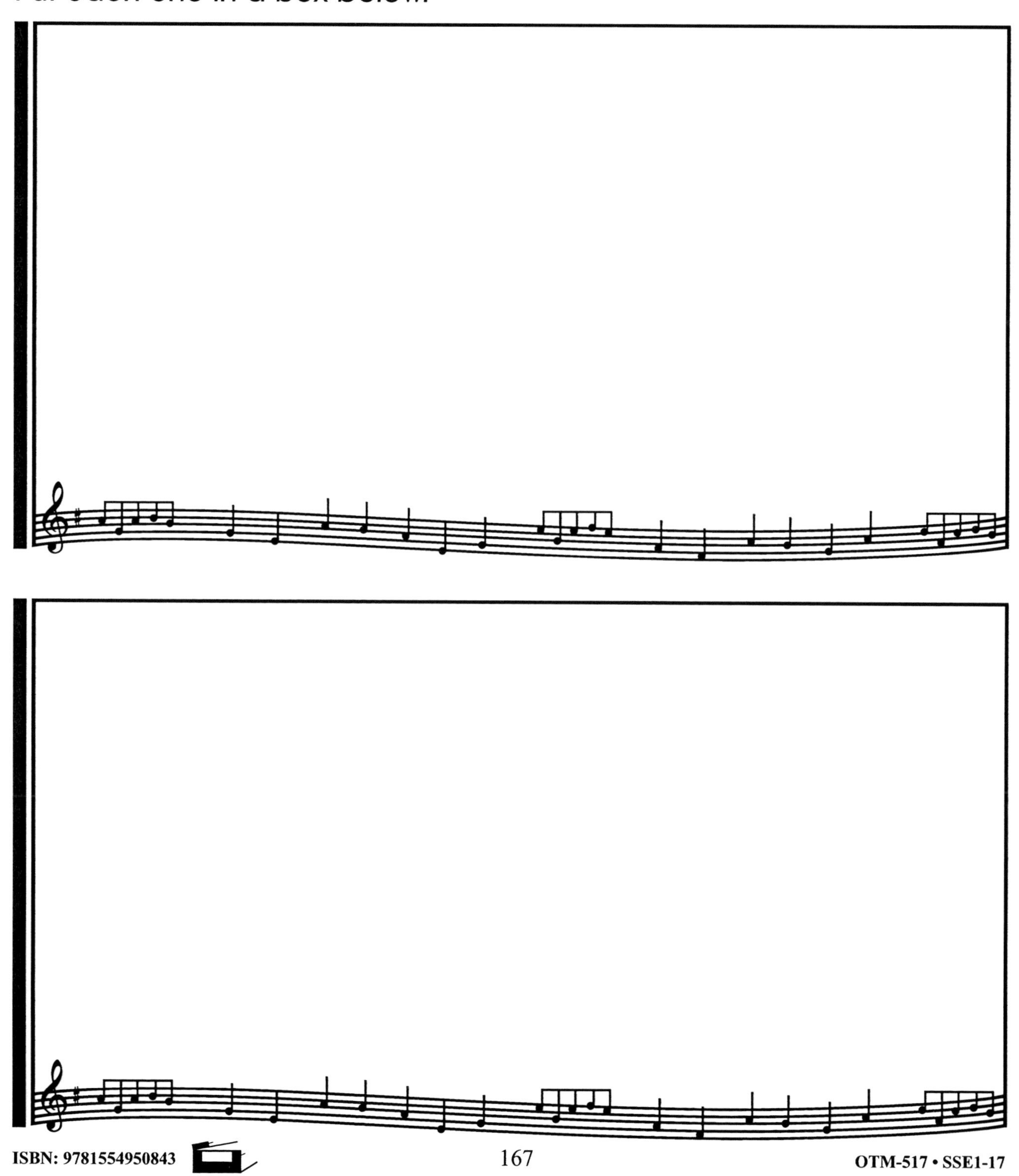

# Answer Key

**Is it 1 or 2?** ***(Page 121)***

10 Circles, 9 Squares

**Sea Song** ***(Page 122)***

5 = orange, 3 = yellow, 4= gray, 6 = green

**Notes to Note** ***(Page 123)***

3, 3, 5, 6, 4, 4

**What Is It?** ***(Page 124)***

a guitar

**One, Two, Beats for You** ***(Page 125)***

a bass clef

**How Do I Make Music** ***(Page 145)***

violin

**My Musical Valentine** ***(Page 149)***

the music alphabet

**The Lucky Rainbow** ***(Page 150)***

from top to bottom: 6, 2, 5, 4, 1, 3

**Fish Beats** ***(Page 153)***

6 yellow fish, 5 orange fish

**Review Quiz** ***(Page 164)***

top to bottom: treble clef, two beat rest, double bar line, one beat rest, one beat note, staff, violin, two beat note, bar line, bass clef

ISBN: 9781554950843

Teacher Notes:

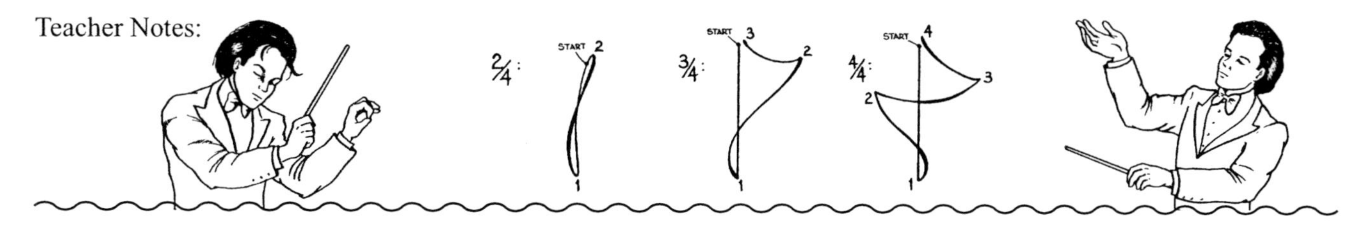


# Developing Music Skills in Grade 3

**Introduction:**

The activities in this book have three goals:

- to encourage students to be creative.
- to promote their enjoyment of music.
- to educate students in the field of music.

Since creativity is very important in music, there will be a variety of ways in which the work will be accomplished. The students should enjoy this program and take a positive approach to music. They may like to take the information home or to other environments. Music is everywhere and is a universal language. The students might be amazed at the effect it has on people's lives and the endless variety of music that exists.

1. Each exercise will have a main point or concept, a sign to learn or a musical activity to finish.
2. If there are small dots, the student is to connect the dots to help them form letters, numbers, signs or directions.
3. A variety of materials are encouraged to be used while completing the activities and worksheets such as crayons, markers, colored paper or other available supplies.
4. The students could make a musical booklet to keep their work altogether and could be later used as a reference.
5. When their booklet or amount of knowledge and activities are completed, the students could receive a certificate with or without testing, depending on the teacher.
6. The games provided will reinforce the knowledge learned.
7. A prize board is a great incentive but is optional.
8. The concepts introduced are:
    - woodwind instruments
    - the one beat note and rest
    - the two beat note and rest
    - the three beat note
    - the brace
    - the bass cleff
    - A B C D E F G
    - singing do to do
    - repeat signs
    - the staff
    - the bar line
    - the double bar line
    - the treble clef
    - pitch
    - the musical alphabet
    - the composer Beethoven

ISBN: 9781554950843 

Teacher Notes:

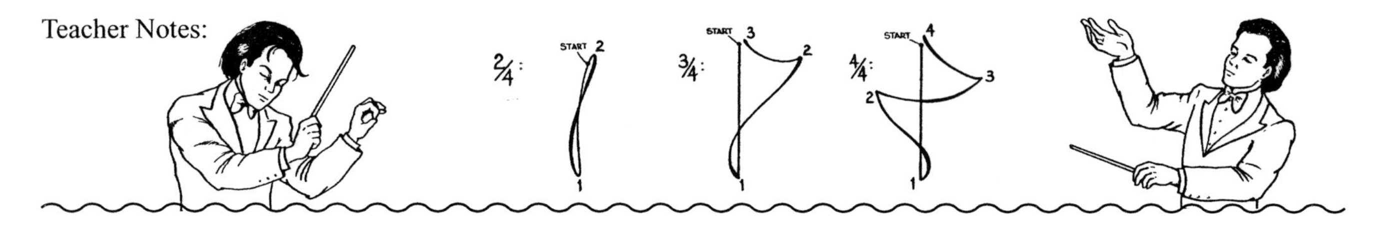


# List of Materials

- Worksheets must be reproduced and completed with a variety of coloring materials.

- Crayons of different textures and colors, markers or pencil crayons of different shades are needed to color the worksheets effectively.

- Graphite pencils will be needed for drawing.

- For the “Vine Flute” you will need thick pieces of vine from pumpkins. They must be 7 to 8 inches (18 cm to 20 cm) in length. You will need one per student. You will also need a pick, of some sort, to hollow it out.

- For the games you will need construction paper, glue, a score page, a tin foil plate, a duotang clip, and an arrow made of plastic.

- The best materials for the stencils are crayons of some sort. If the stencils are being used under paper, regular crayons are great to shade on the top sheet to make designs. If the stencils are being traced by the students, they will need pencil crayons or a pencil and regular crayons to color. The stencils need to be glued or stapled onto a heavy backing as they wear out quickly. Extra copies should be made.

- Incentives, such as prizes for a prize board, are great to stimulate interest in the subject. The prize board would have to be prepared with construction paper and colored material. Prizes could include stickers, erasers, small toys or other small items.

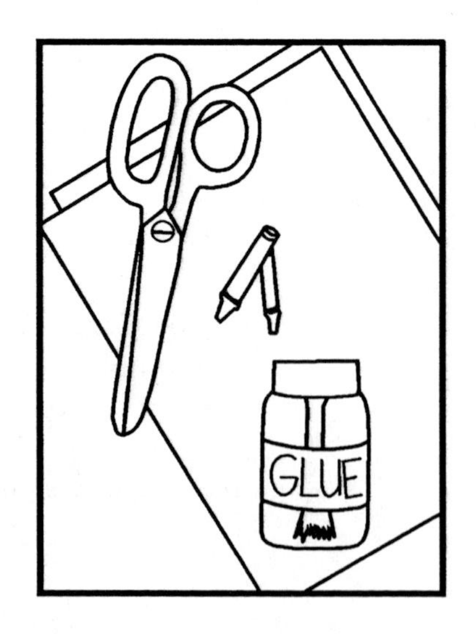

Teacher Notes:

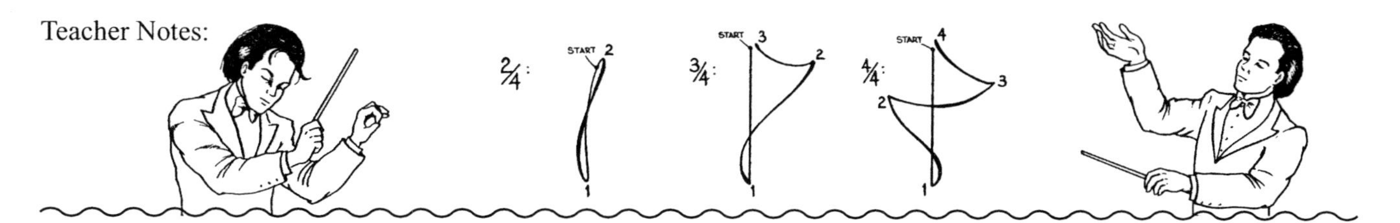


# Teaching Suggestions

Any of the following ideas can be used in the classroom to motivate student interest in music.

- Display pictures of musical signs, woodwind instruments, and musicians in the classroom.
- Become familiar with the music terms at this level.
- Try having the students work individually, in groups or as a class.
- If working in groups, rotate the groups at different work stations.
- Make sure each work station is provided with the necessary equipment.
- Make the vine flutes before doing the work on the woodwind instruments.
- Students with some knowledge of music should be grouped with students who do not have any knowledge of music.
- Assemble the games and game boards ahead of time.
- Encourage the students to think of music at home and in other environments.
- Encourage creativity and enjoyment at all times.
- If possible bring instruments into the classroom. Perhaps a musician who plays a woodwind instrument could visit your class to demonstrate how one is played and the sound that it makes.

Teacher Notes:

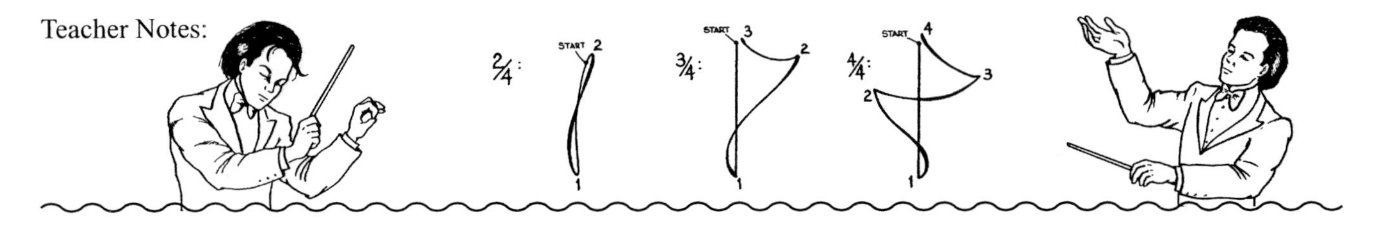


# Music Glossary

**Bar Line:** The bar line is a vertical line separating music into two sections. These sections are based on the timing of the song.

**Bass Clef:** The bass clef is used for the lowest instruments or the low end of the keyboard. The bass clef circles around the F line and is sometimes called the "F clef."

**Brace:** This is a bracket, at the beginning of music, connecting more than one staff. Many times a treble clef and bass clef will be connected by a brace.

**Composer:** A composer is a song-writer from the past or present day.

**Double Bar Line:** A double bar line is two bar lines at the end of the song.

**High and Low Pitch:** Some instruments play in a higher range or pitch just like some voices have a higher range or pitch. The high range uses the treble clef and the low range uses the bass clef. For some voicing or instruments in between these ranges other clefs are used.

**Notes:** When you see a note, there needs to be a sound made by an instrument or voice.

**One Beat:** One beat is one count, like the tick of a clock.

**One Beat Rest:** When resting for one beat, there needs to be a period of silence for the count of one.

**Repeat Signs:** Sometimes there will be a repeat sign at the end of a song which would mean to repeat the entire song. Other times there will be two repeat signs. Everything in between the signs are to be repeated.

Teacher Notes:

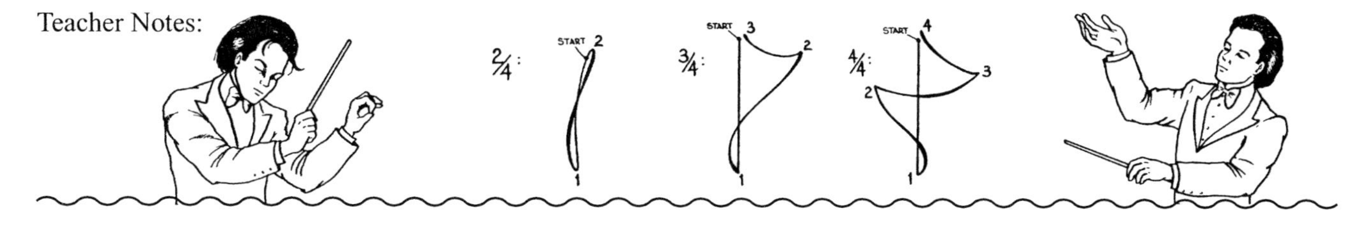


# Music Glossary

**Rests:** Rests are periods of silence.

**Staff:** The staff is five lines and four spaces that music is written on. Sometimes more than one staff is connected and they will be called "staves."

**Three Beat Notes:** A three beat note would sound on the count of one and be held for two and three counts.

**Treble Clef:** The treble clef is used for the highest pitched instruments or the higher end of key-board instruments. The middle point of the treble clef centers around the G line of the staff and sometimes can be called the "G clef."

**Two Beat Notes:** Tick tock would therefore be two beats or two counts. When holding a note for longer than one beat the note should sound on the count of one and held for the remainder of the time.

**Two Beat Rests:** When resting for two beats, there needs to be a period of silence for two beats.

**Woodwind Instruments:** These instruments originally were made out of wood, but today they are made from different types of metals. The sound is made from air passing through tubing. Holes are opened and closed to change the pitch. Reeds are used with many woodwind instruments. This is on the mouthpiece and has to be replaced often. The reed vibrates. The piccolo, flute, clarinet, oboe, and bassoon are the main woodwind instruments in an orchestra. The saxophone is also a woodwind instrument although it is made of brass. It uses a reed.

# The Vine Flute

## Teacher Instructions

### List of Material Needed:

- thick pieces of pumpkin vine that are 7 or 8 inches (18 to 20 cm) in length.
- a pick, of some sort, is also needed to hollow out the vine and to make the holes.

### Instructions:

1. The vines need to be hollowed out. At the discretion of the teacher, this can be done by the student with a pick or this can be done for the students. The students then can make the holes in the vine with scissors or another sharp tool.

2. The holes should be about the size of the end of your ring finger. There should be three holes on the top and one hole on the bottom.

3. Blow in one end of the flute and cover up some holes. Then blow again changing the holes to be closed and the pitch.

Teacher Notes:

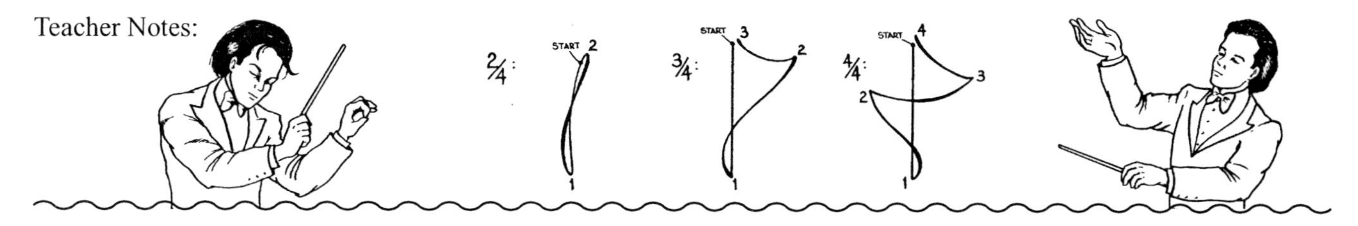


# Musical Elements

This section deals with the following musical elements:

- the one beat note
- the one beat rest
- the two beat note
- the two beat rest
- the three beat note
- the treble clef
- the bass clef
- music signs of the staff

1. There are two display sheets found on pages 176 and 177 that could be photocopied, colored, and mounted on a colorful sturdy backing and laminated. They could be displayed in the classroom for all the students to see. These sheets could also be photocopied and added to the students' music booklets.

2. The exercise on the one beat, two beat, and three beat note should be done after explaining what one beat is. This is explained on the page called "1, 2, 3" found on page 178. It is then followed by the exercise called "Rhythm Plus" found on page 179.

3. The exercise called "Balloon Beat" on page 180 demonstrates the difference between the three types of notes and their values.

4. The worksheets called "Notes to Note" on page 181 and "Who's Under the Rainbow?" on page 182 consist of adding the values of the notes and coloring specific areas that have these values.

5. The worksheets called "Trebles" on page 183 and "Clef Around" on page 184 are to reinforce the recognition and the making of the treble clef and the bass clef.

6. The worksheet called "Brace to Face" on page 185 is to show the difference between the brace and the one beat rest. They are similar in shape but are opposite. The faces will help the students to remember them.

7. The worksheet called "Repeat and Repeat" on page 186 will help the students to notice the difference between a repeat sign and a bar line or double bar line.

8. The "Stencils" found on page 187 should be photocopied and mounted on a sturdy backing and laminated for student usage. Multiple copies should be made as the Stencils wear out quickly. Using the Stencils can be fun and creative for the students. This exercise may be done individually or in groups. The students could turn the Stencils into insects, creatures, animals, garden flowers etc. This exercise will spark the imaginations of the students. Cards could also be made for special occasions.

# Notes and Rests

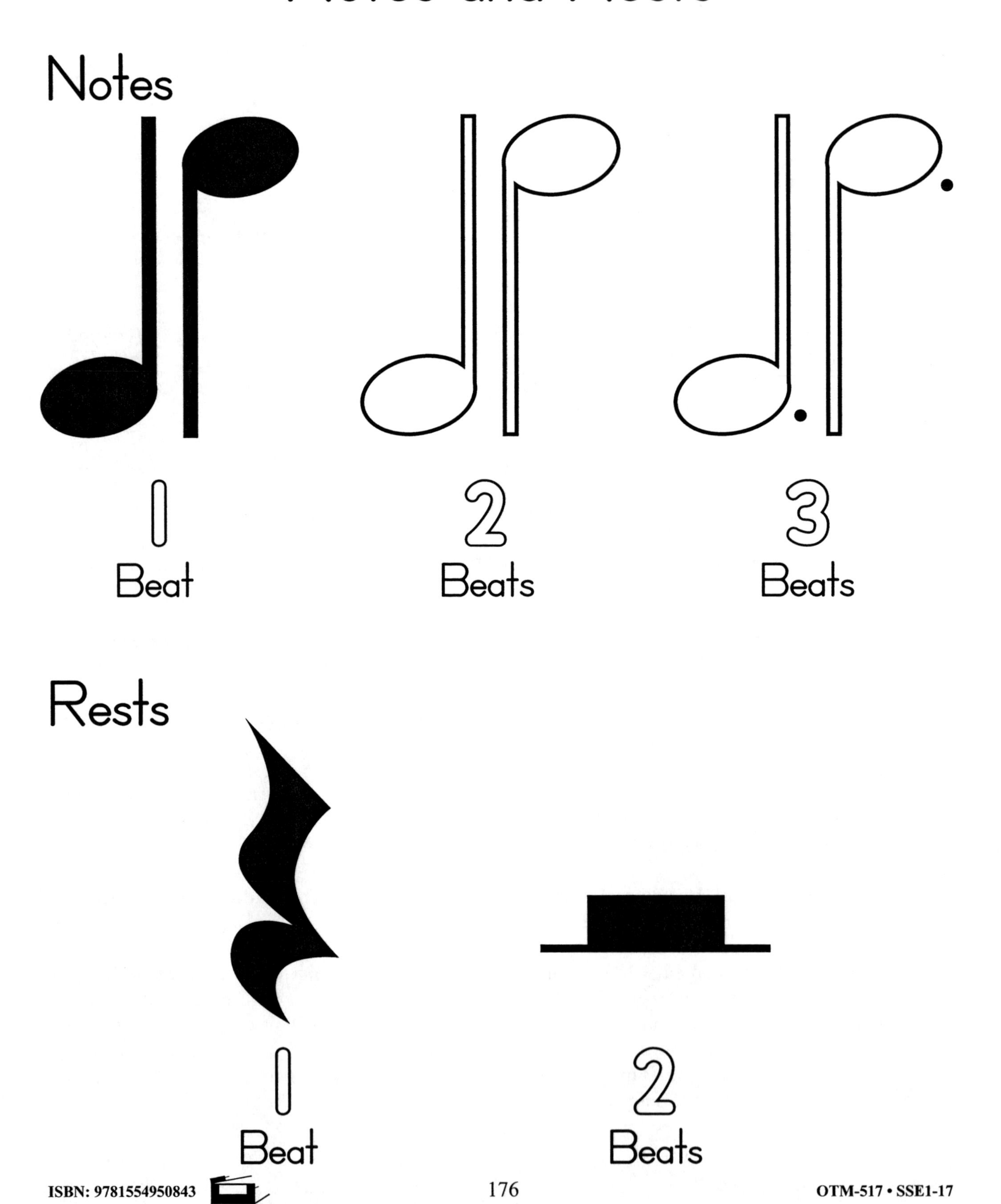

# Musical Signs

## The Staff

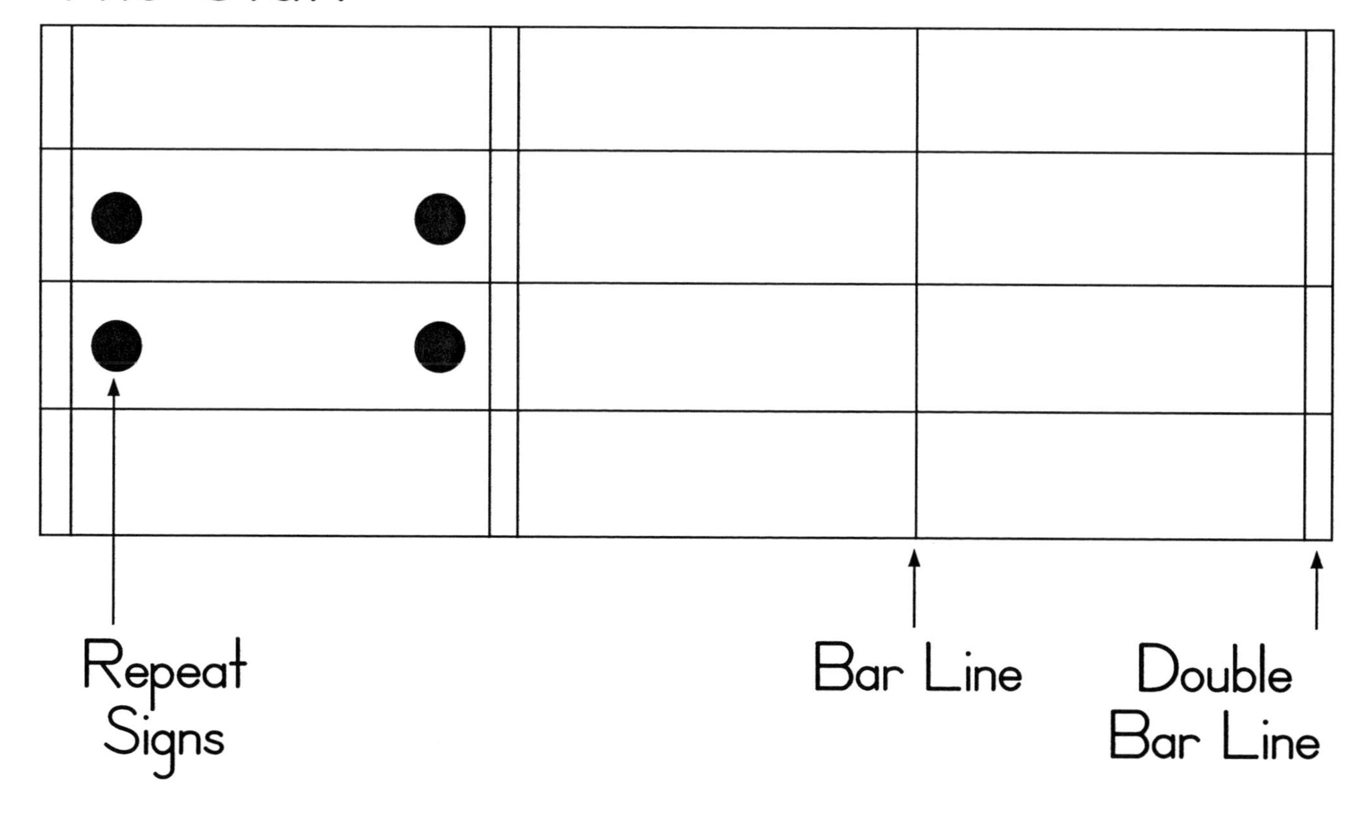

  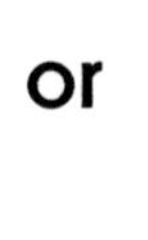 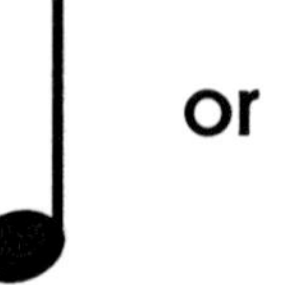  

**Tick** **Boom** or or or

1 **One beat =** <u>tick</u> or <u>boom</u> or <u>la</u> or <u>rest</u>

2 **Two beats =** <u>tick, tock</u> or <u>boom, boom</u>

**or** = <u>la, la</u> or <u>rest, rest</u>

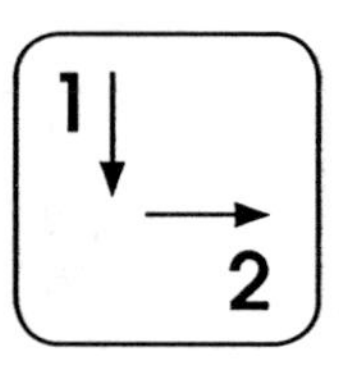


When you sing or play a two beat note you have to hold the note for two counts.

You press or begin making the sound on one and hold during two.

This note would be held for two beats and so would this rest. A two beat rest is held for two beats of silence.

3 **Three beats =** <u>tick, tock, tick</u> or <u>boom, boom, boom</u>

**or** = <u>la, la, la</u> or <u>rest, rest, rest</u>

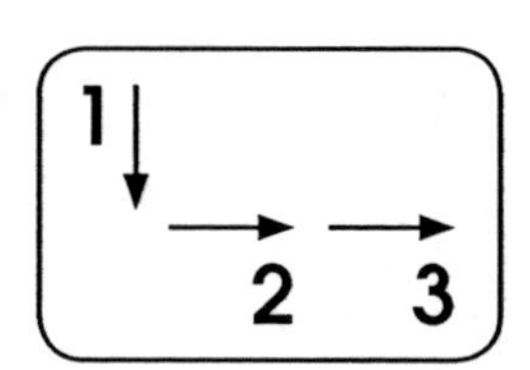


This is a 3 beat note . It has a dot after it.

To sing or play a three beat note you start on one and hold for two, three.

Get a partner and hum while they count 1, 2, 3.

You are singing a three beat note.

# Rhythm Plus

Tap with sticks or clap with hands.

One beat note tap once. Two beat notes will be tap, hold. Rest is silence.

T = Tap     TH = Tap, Hold     R = Rest     RR = Rest, Rest

Group 1:

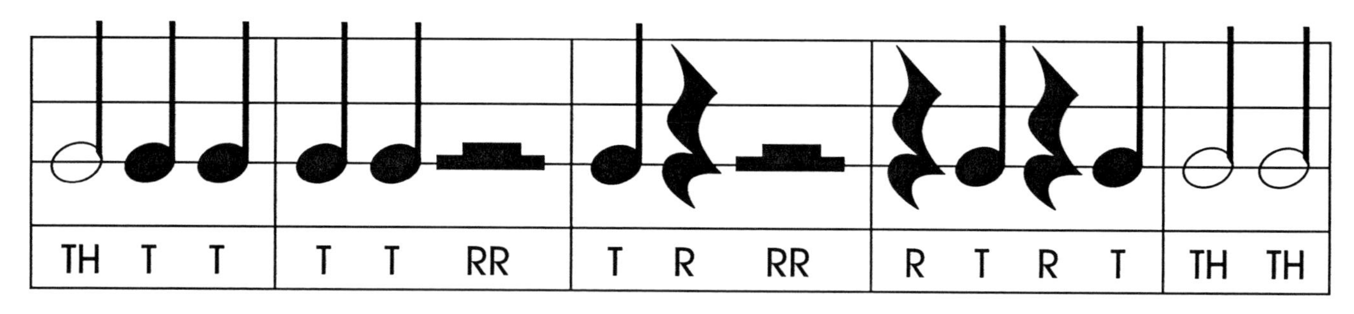


Split students into groups. This can be practised individually or all the groups together.

Group 2:

Group 3:

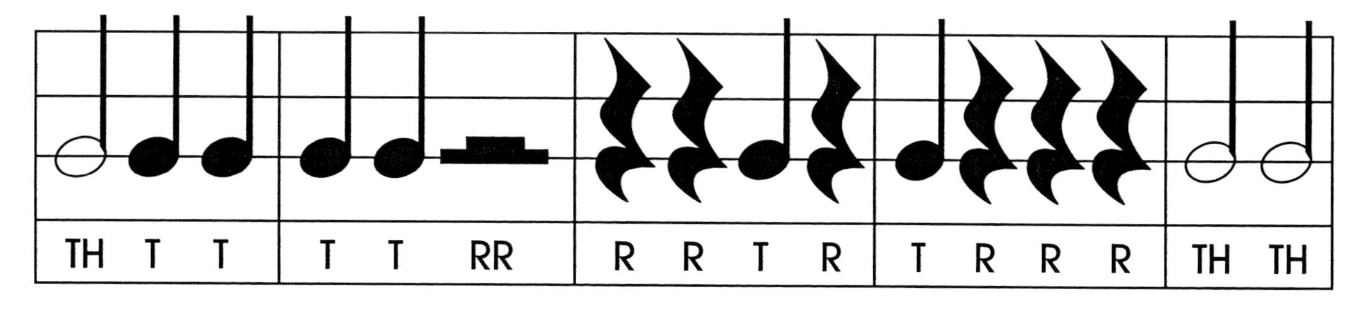

# Balloon Beat

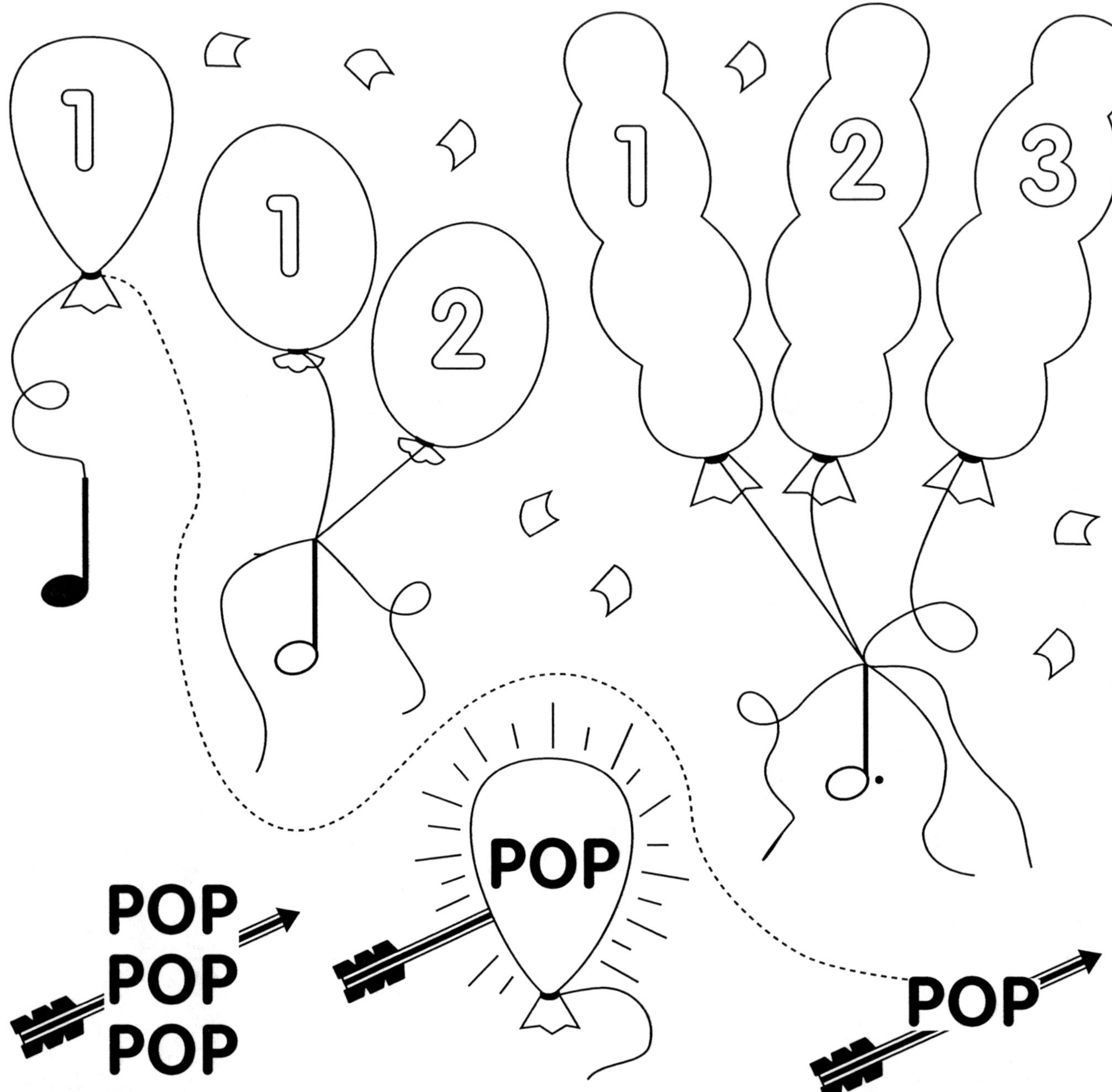


Draw a line from this arrow to the 3 balloons for 3 beats "pop, pop, pop."

Draw a line from this arrow to the 2 balloons which would go "pop, pop" in 2 beats.

One beat is like the popping of one balloon. Draw a solid line from the arrow to the balloon.

# Notes to Note

𝅗𝅥. + 𝅗𝅥 = ______

𝄽 + 𝅗𝅥. + ♩ = ______

𝅗𝅥 + 𝅗𝅥 + 𝄼 = ______

𝅗𝅥. + ♩ + 𝄽 = ______

♩ + 𝅗𝅥 + 𝅗𝅥. = ______

𝄽 + 𝄼 + 𝅗𝅥. = ______

# Who's Under the Rainbow?

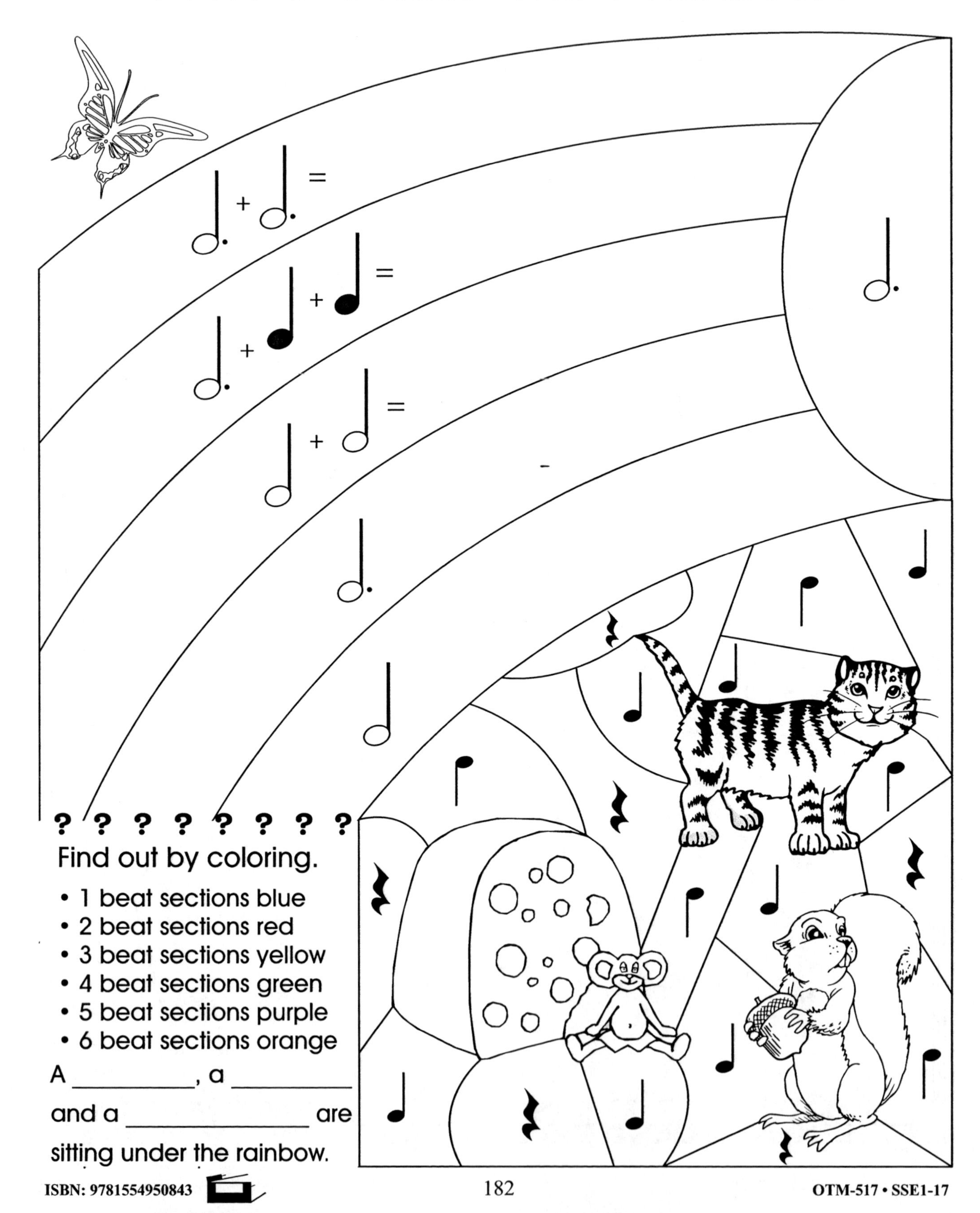

# Trebles

Trace the treble clefs that are getting smaller and smaller.

End End End End

Start Start Start Start

Try to draw four more treble clefs below on the staff.

ISBN: 9781554950843

# Clef Around

Trace the bass clefs below going round and round.
Make the design into something.

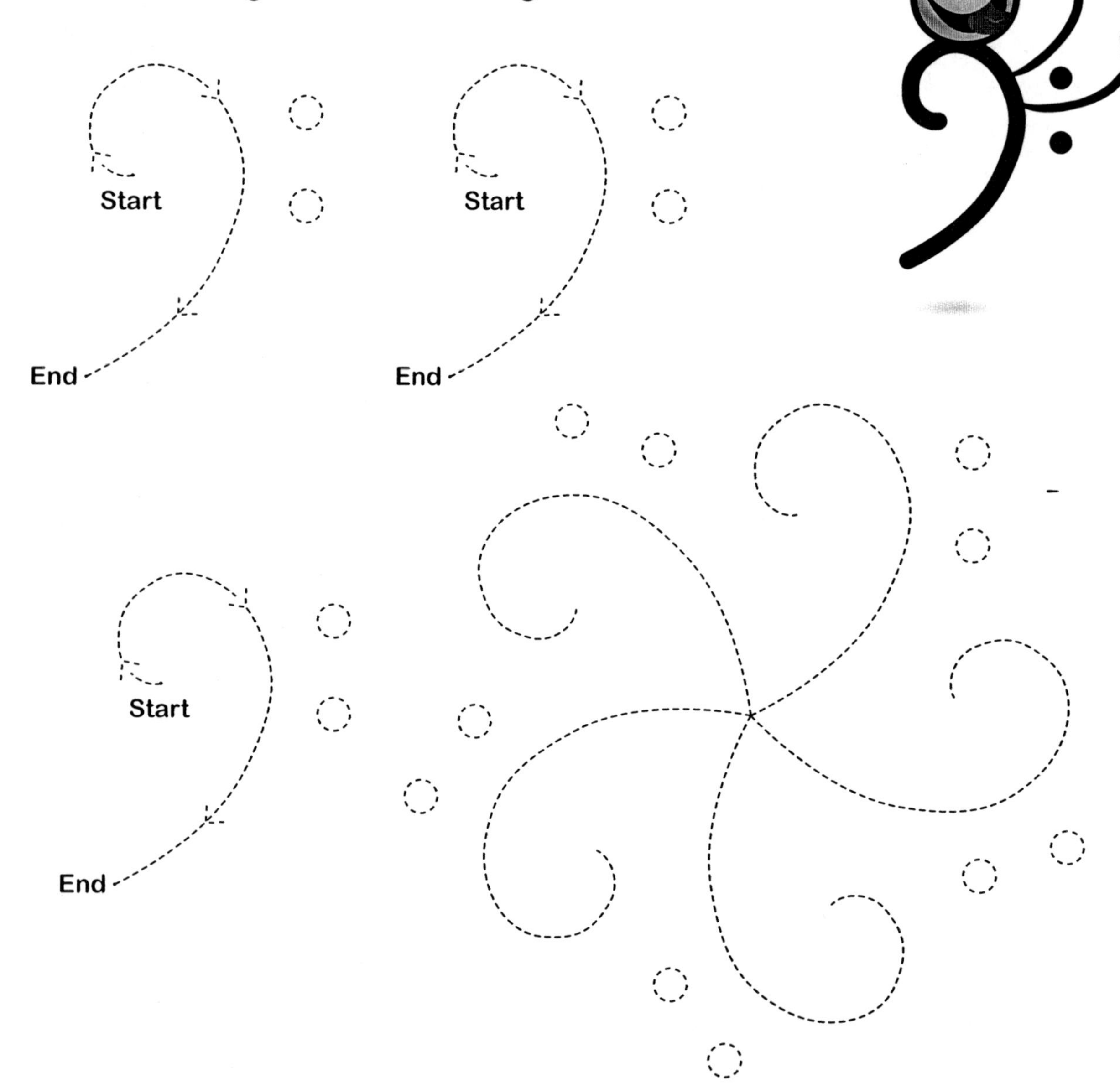


Try to draw four more bass clefs on the staff below.

ISBN: 9781554950843

# Brace to Face

This is a brace. It joins more than one staff together.

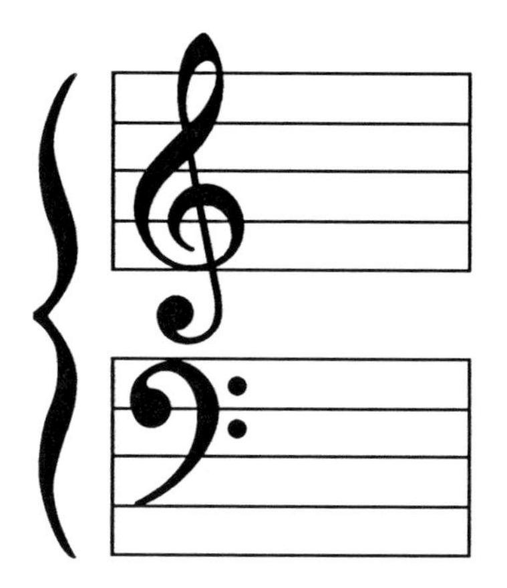

This is a one beat rest.

This is an old face. "Old" and "one beat" both start with the letter "O."

This is a baby face. Baby and brace both start with the letter "B."

Draw a face and name it starting with the letter "O."

______________________

Draw a face and name it starting with the letter "B."

______________________

# Repeat and Repeat

Draw the opposite, of what you see on the right side of the staff, on the left side of the staff.

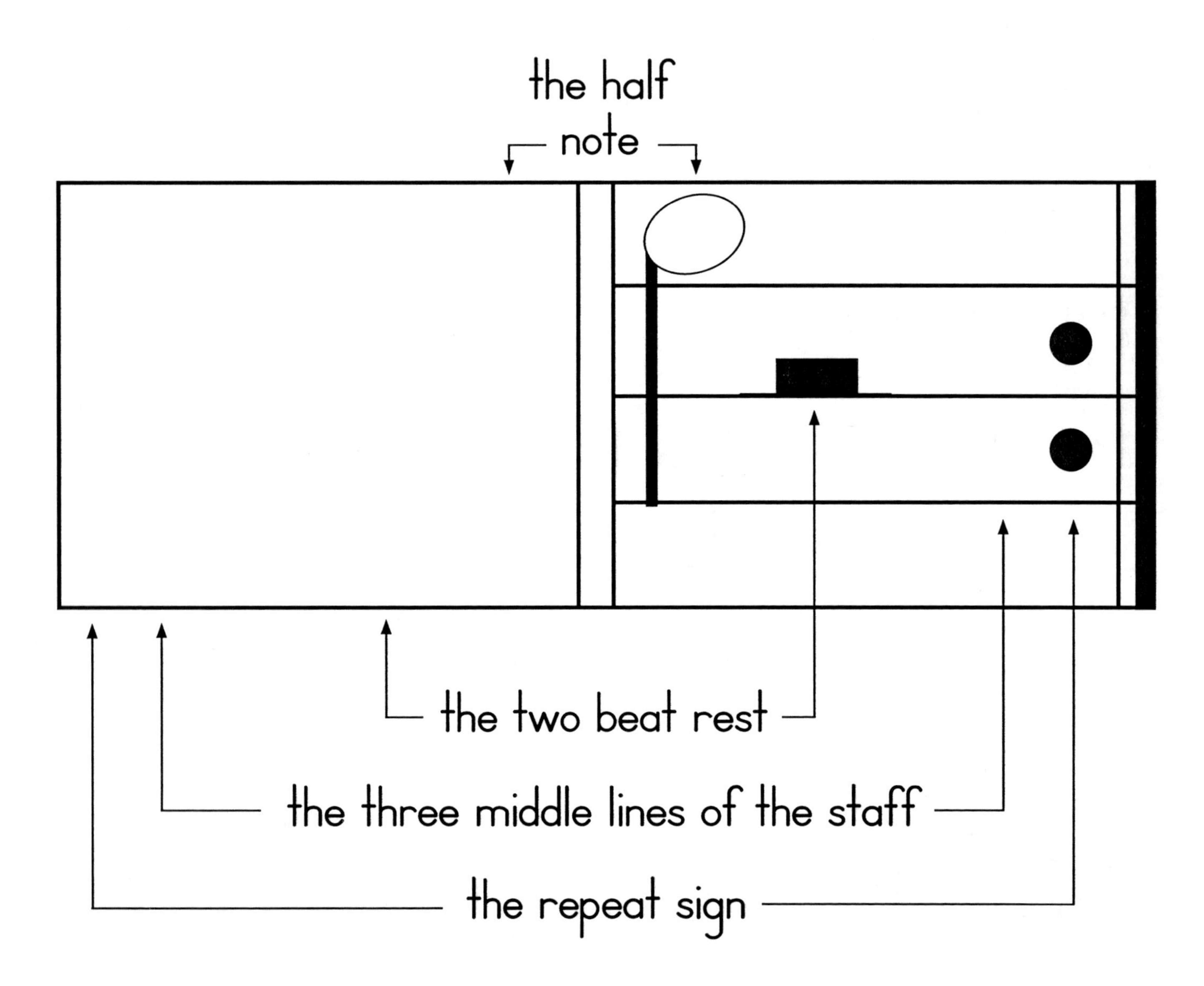


When you have finished you will have two repeat signs on each end of the music.

This means the music would be played twice.

# STENCILS

Teacher Notes:

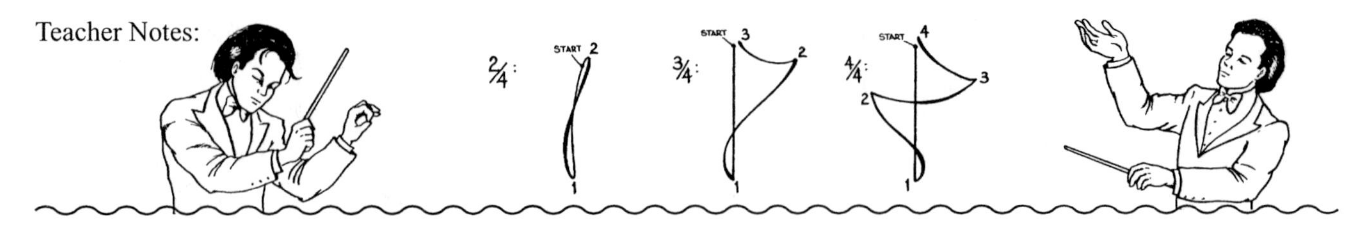

# Developing Music Skills in Grade 3

- Woodwind Instruments
- The Two Scales
- The Composer

- The story called "The Royal Joke," which can be found on pages 189-191, is about woodwind instrument characters. These characters will introduce the students to the woodwind family. The pages can be photocopied and made into storybooks for the students to color and read or they may be used as part of a music booklet.

- The teacher should try to have some woodwind instruments on hand to show the class. Perhaps a local musician, who plays a woodwind instrument, could be invited to the classroom to play for the students and to discuss how the instrument is played. Perhaps one of the students in the class is learning how to play a woodwind instrument and it could be brought to school.

- The making and playing of a vine flute will add enjoyment and interest to this section as well.

- The worksheets in this section will provide a review of counting by 2's and alphabetical order (page 192); problem solving (pages 193 and 195); the three beat note (page 194).

- "The Musical Spelling" sheet on page 196 has been designed to help the student remember the seven letters used in music, the musical words, and their spellings.

- The "Do Re Me, A B C" song is about the two scales used in music. One is the music scale and the other is the singing scale. They can be said as rhymes or if the teacher can read music, they can be sung. The music is very simple for this song. It could also be demonstrated on a keyboard by someone who can read music.

- The composer, Beethoven, is also introduced in this book. The booklet called "Beethoven and Me" found on pages 198 to 201 can be photocopied and made into storybooks for the students to read and color. Learning history can be boring for young students but if they can relate the facts to themselves, it becomes more interesting. The students are to read the facts about Beethoven and then answer the questions about themselves. This will help them to remember the facts about the composer.

- To acquaint your students with Beethoven's music, play such melodies as "Ode to Joy," "Fur Elise," or "The Fifth Symphony" which has very famous four notes at the beginning.

# The Royal Joke

The woodwind section was the town's Royal Family. Princess Ownia Oboe was always skipping through the palace singing in her high pitched voice. The birds loved to hear her sing and they would chirp along with her.

Her little sister Flora Flute would sometimes sing along with her and they would sing a duet. Patty Piccolo, the smallest and the youngest would try to sing too but all that came out was a high soft squeek. She was so tiny and cute.

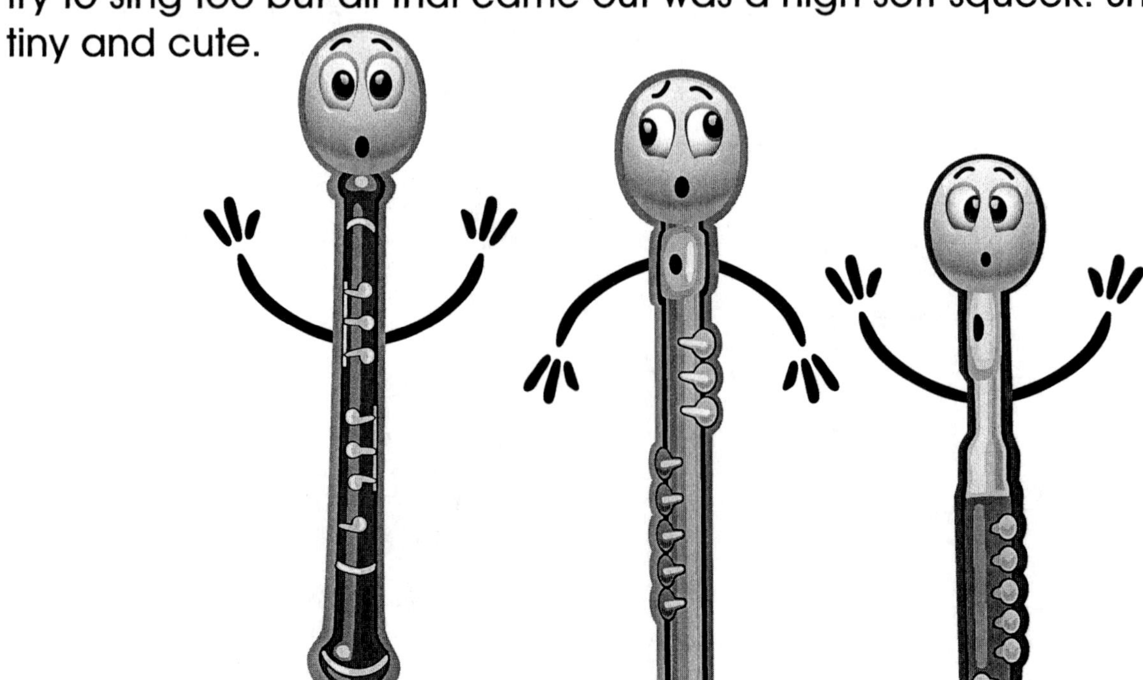

Cleo Clarinet, the Town Joker, was always trying to make everyone in the Palace laugh. He could change his voice into different characters.

One day, however, King Bruno Bassoon played a trick on Cleo. Bruno hid in some bushes and pretended to be a wild animal. Bassoons can make very strange low sounds so this was an easy task. Cleo started running through the woods, screaming in his highest pitched voice, which could be pretty high and loud.

King Bruno kept running ahead and making animal sounds from behind the bushes. Finally he jumped out in front of Cleo and startled him. Cleo let out a scream and then they both started laughing, because Cleo was the joker, after all.

# What Am I?

Connect the dots by counting by 2's and connect the letters of the alphabet.

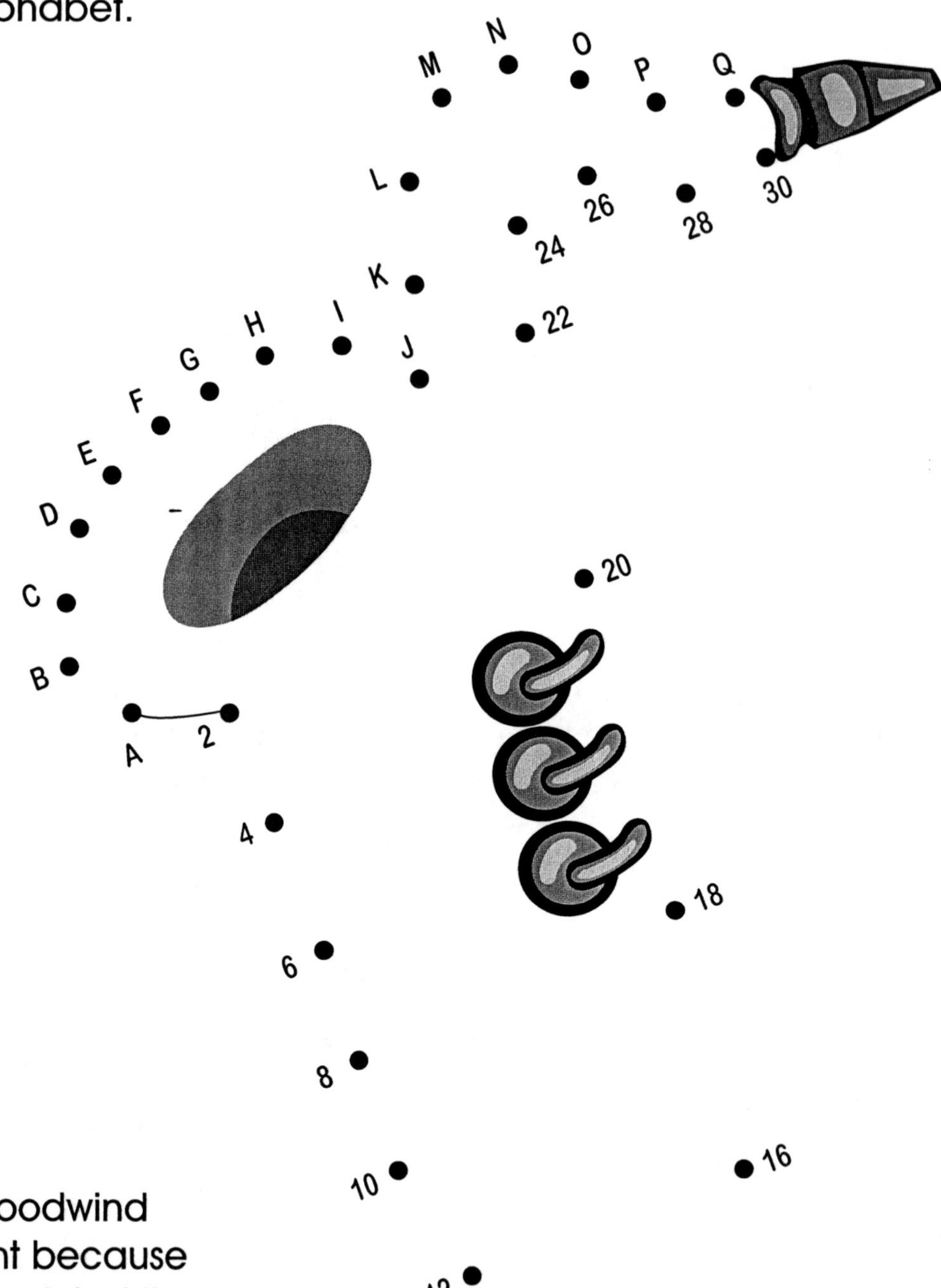


I am a woodwind instrument because I use a reed, but I'm made of brass.

I am a ___ ___ ___ ___ ___ ___ ___ ___ ___.

# The Gift

Flora Flute was walking Saxy, her pet, when she noticed a music stand in the store window.

Flora had eleven toonies in her purse.

A toonie is $2.00.

She wants to buy Patti, her sister, the music stand.

Can Flora buy the music stand for Patti? ________

How much money does Flora have? ________

How much change will she get back when she buys the stand. ________

# The Three Beat Note

Make three notes with the ends of my hat into three beat notes.

Do you know what 3 x 3 =_____ ?

Color the picture neatly.

# Beat the Note

The Woodwind sisters are playing the "Beat the Note" game.

The game is $2.00 each try.

If each girl played two games how much would it cost them all together?

It would cost them __________.

Everytime the board is hit 10 seconds of music is played.

How long would the music play in total for the girls?

It would play for _________ seconds.

Color the picture neatly.

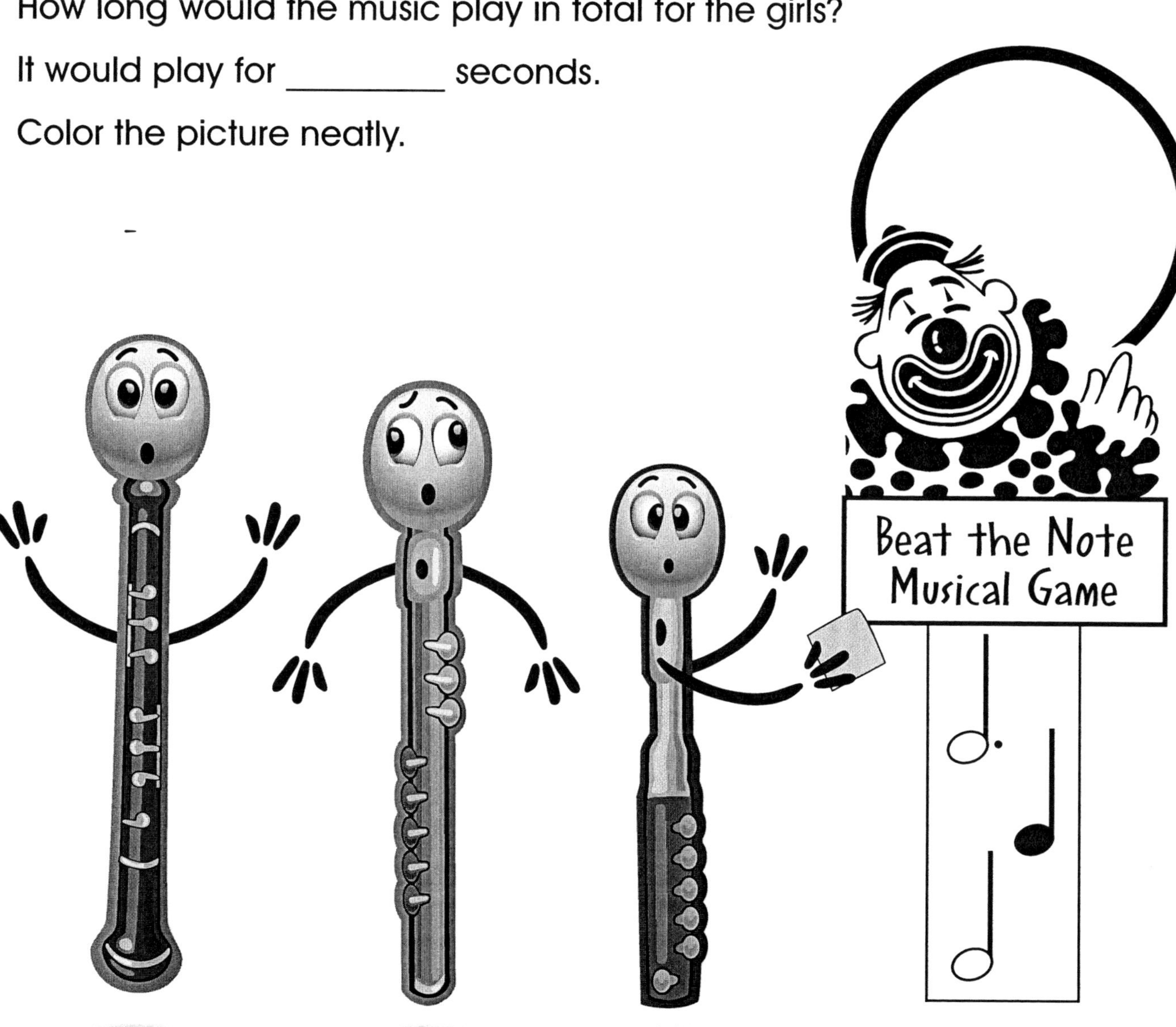

# Musical Spelling

Fill in the spaces with the letters below to make musical words.
You can use the letters more than once.

A B C D E F G

1. O ___ O E
2. S I N ___ I N ___
3. R ___ S T
4. ___ L A R I N E T
5. T R E ___ L E C L ___ F
6. T H R E E B E ___ T S
7. ___ R U M S
8. ___ A R L I N E
9. N O T ___ S
10. S T ___ F F
11. B ___ S S C L ___ F
12. P I T ___ H

ISBN: 9781554950843

# Do Re Me, A B C

G
do
F
ti
E
la
D
sol
C
fa
B
mi
re
A
do
One, two, three
Do, Re, Mi,
One, two, three,
Do, Re, Mi.
To the top we go
Fa, Sol, La, Ti, Do.
A, B, C
1, 2, 3
A, B, C,
1, 2, 3,
D, E, F, and G
Notes for you and me.
4 x's
Play Twice

# Beethoven and Me

Beethoven was born in Germany. His father taught him the piano when he was four years old.

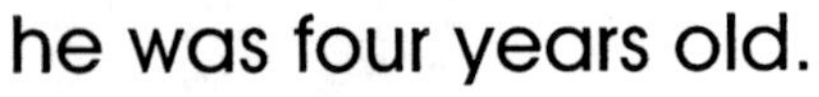

Where were you born? ____________________________

Do you play an instrument? ________________________

ISBN: 9781554950843

Beethoven started to go deaf when he was twenty. He could not hear as well.

How would you feel if you were deaf? ______________________

Beethoven would jump all over with excitement when he conducted music.

Would you like to be a conductor of an orchestra? __________

Beethoven was often stubborn and wanted his own way.

Are you ever stubborn? ______________________________

Because of Beethoven's character, he remained single his whole life. He did write a song because of a woman. It is believed that his song called "Fur Elise" was inspired by a woman.

Have you ever written a song for anyone? ____________________

Would you like to? ______________________________

One of Beethoven's favorite foods was macaroni.

What is your favorite food? ___________________________

Why do you like it? ___________________________

Beethoven was an untidy person. Even his handwriting was also messy.

Do you clean your bedroom? ___________________________

Are you a messy person? ___________________________

ISBN: 9781554950843

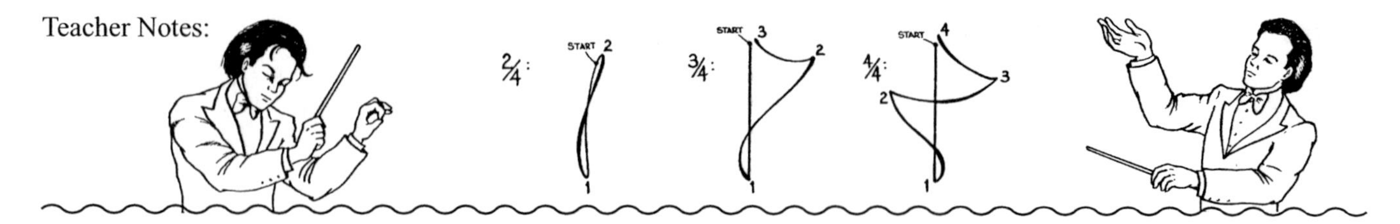


# Holiday Worksheets

- The holiday worksheets found on pages 203 to 209 are a review of all the musical facts learned.
- The "A to G  Halloween," found on page 203, is based on the music alphabet. It will help students to remember which seven letters are used in music.
- The Christmas tree, found on page 204, is to be decorated using the music signs that are on the tree stand. The decorations should cover the entire tree.
- The "Happy New Year" worksheet, found on pages 205, is an addition and subtraction exercise pertaining to beats. This exercise will help students to remember the value of notes and rests.
- "My Musical Valentine" is a word search found on page 206. First the heart must be finished with a solid line connecting all the music signs, then the students are to look for words that are musical terms.
- The "Create New Colors"  worksheet, found on page 207, will help the students learn music signs and will teach them all about blending colors. When finished it could be made into a valentine.
- The "Who was Born on Easter Morn" worksheet, found on page 208, has been designed to help students learn note and rest value.
- The "Lost at Sea" worksheet, found on page 209, is to help the students to recognize the difference between the brace and a one beat rest.
- Holiday worksheets are always exciting for the students. Their imagination should run free and their creativity soar.

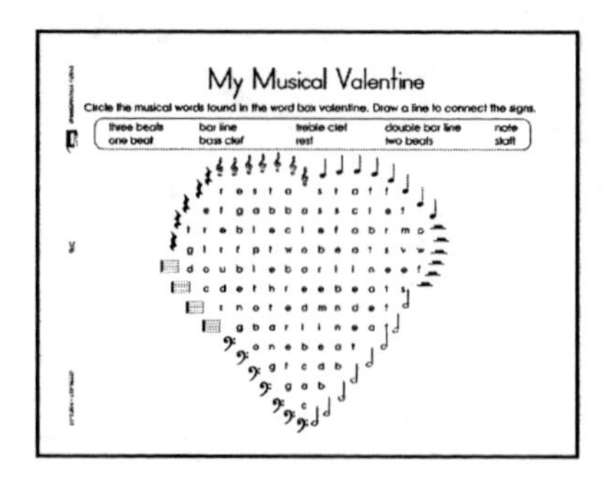

# A to G Halloween

The music alphabet is A B C D E F G. There are seven treats in the bag that start with some of these letters. Print their names on the lines below.

Three letters in the music alphabet are not used. Print their names.

Draw three treats in or around the Halloween bag that begin with these three letters. Print their names too.

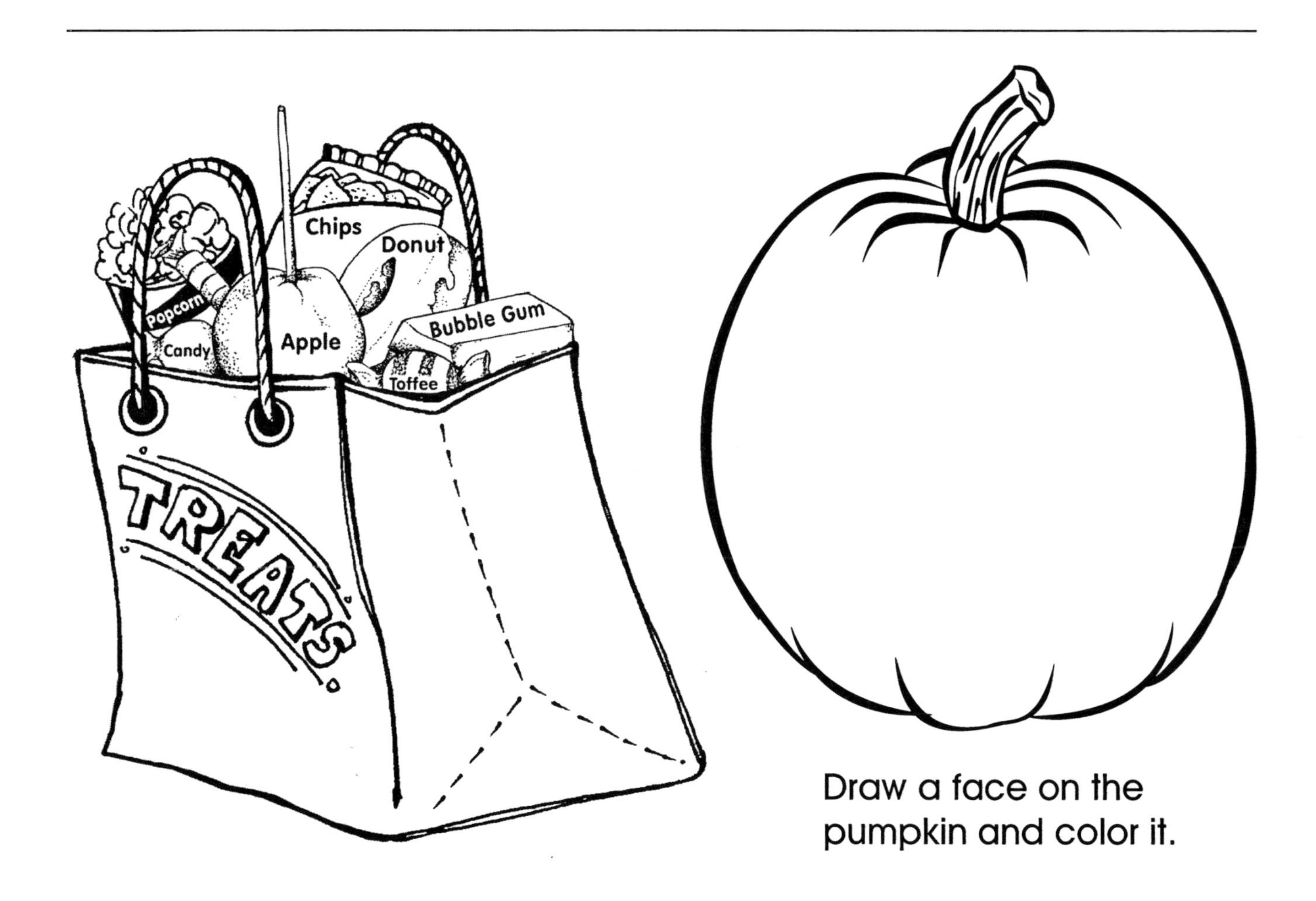


Draw a face on the pumpkin and color it.

ISBN: 9781554950843

# The Musical Christmas Tree

Decorate the tree with notes, rests, and clefs and then color.

ISBN: 9781554950843

# Happy New Year!

Complete the musical addition and subtraction questions found in the horns and balloons. Color them using the color code for the answers.

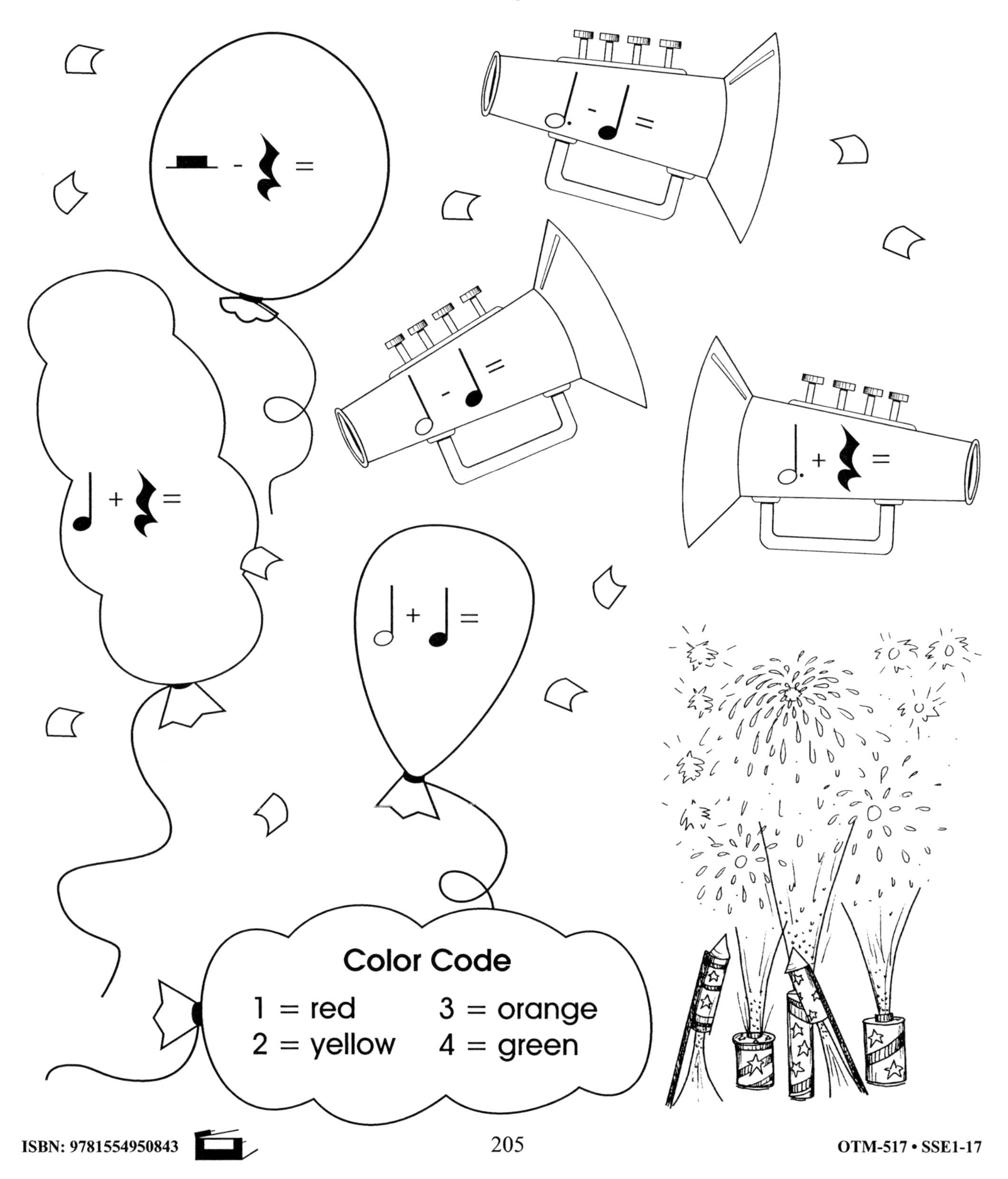


ISBN: 9781554950843

# My Musical Valentine

Circle the musical words found in the word box valentine. Draw a line to connect the signs.

| three beats | bar line | treble clef | double bar line | note |
|---|---|---|---|---|
| one beat | bass clef | rest | two beats | staff |

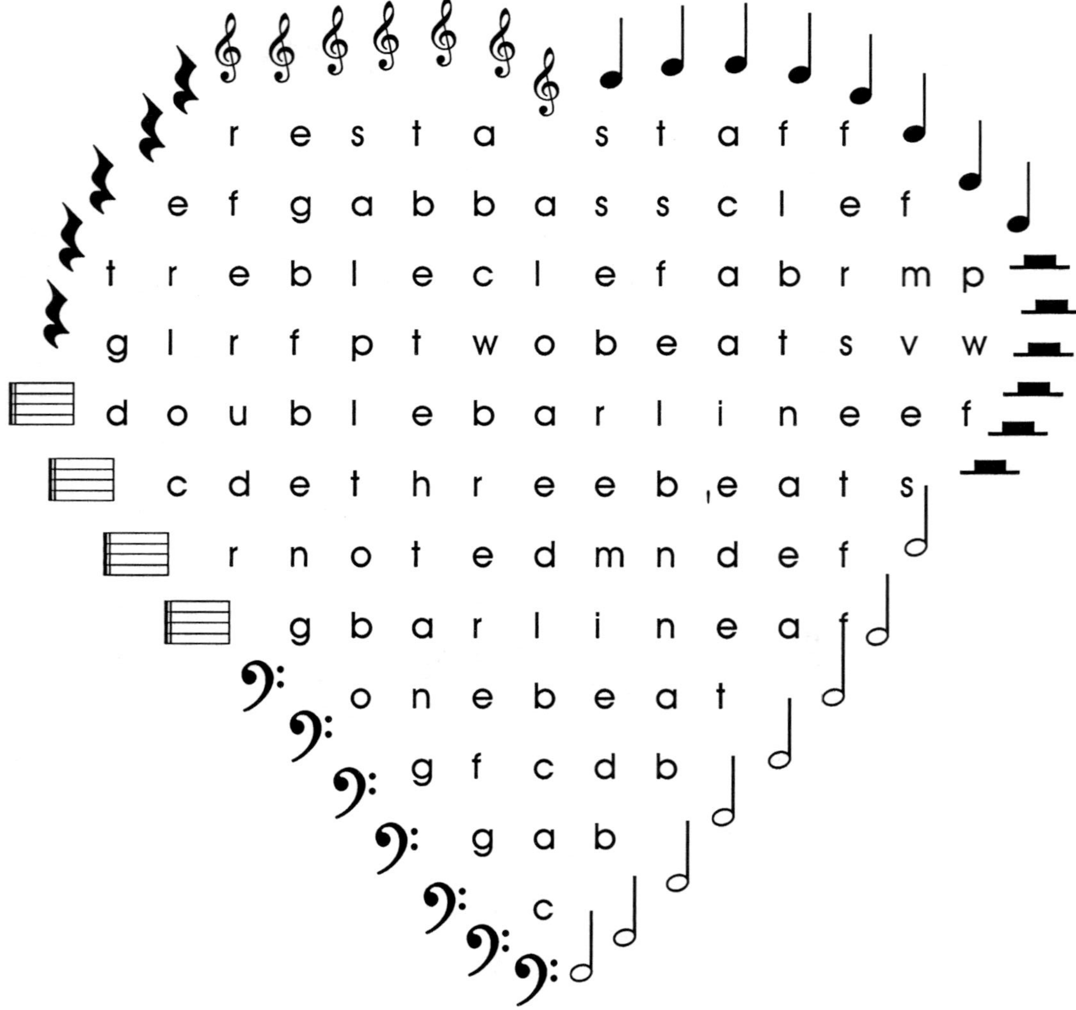


ISBN: 9781554950843

# Create New Colors

Read the signs and color accordingly. Color all of the hearts to blend with the petals.

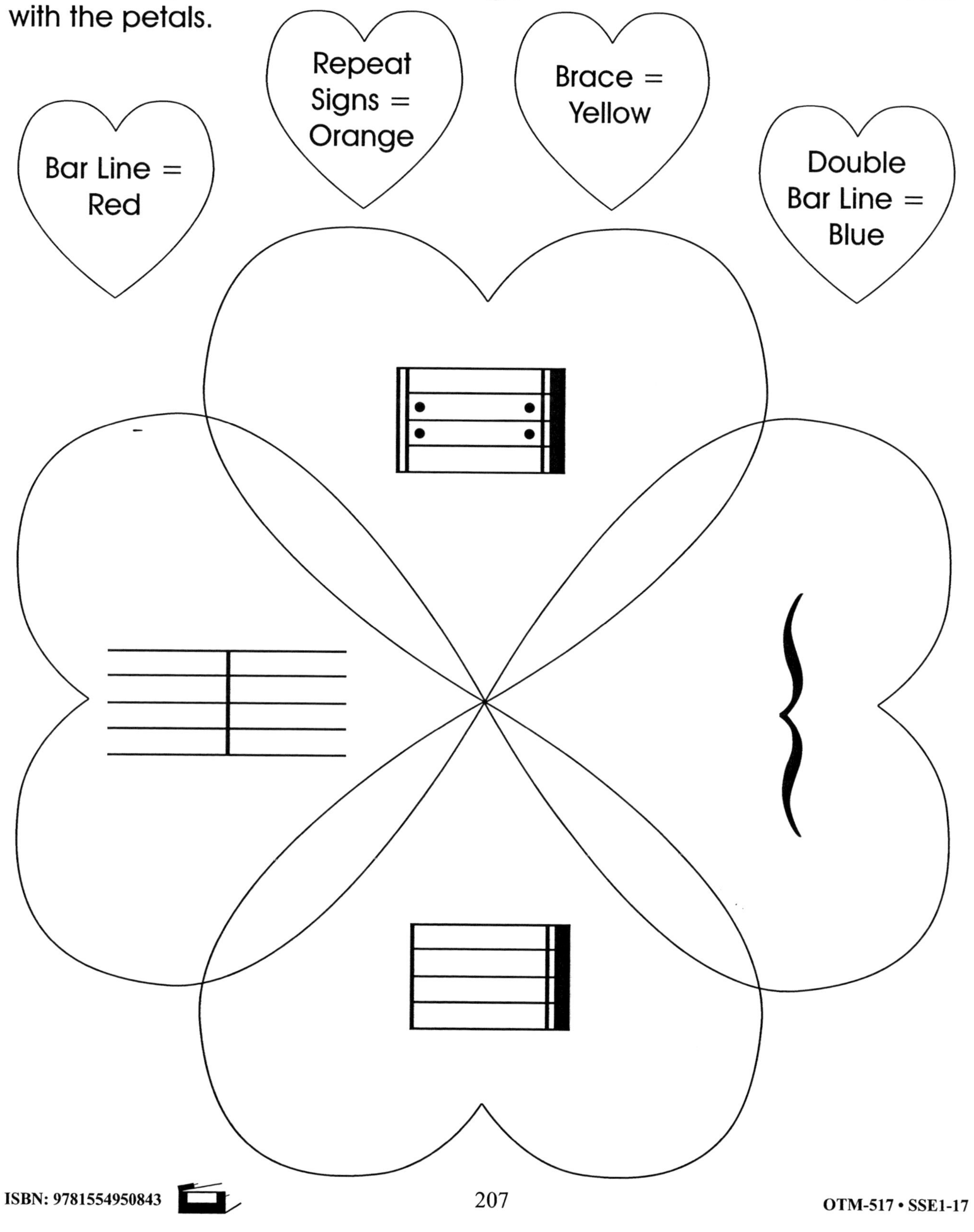


ISBN: 9781554950843

# Who was Born on Easter Morn?

Color the picture according to the code and then finish the picture.

Who was born on Easter morn?

______________________

1 beat = green

2 beats = brown

3 beats = blue

ISBN: 9781554950843

# Lost at Sea

Help the starfish find the other starfish. Follow the brace signs.

Be careful of the shape!!

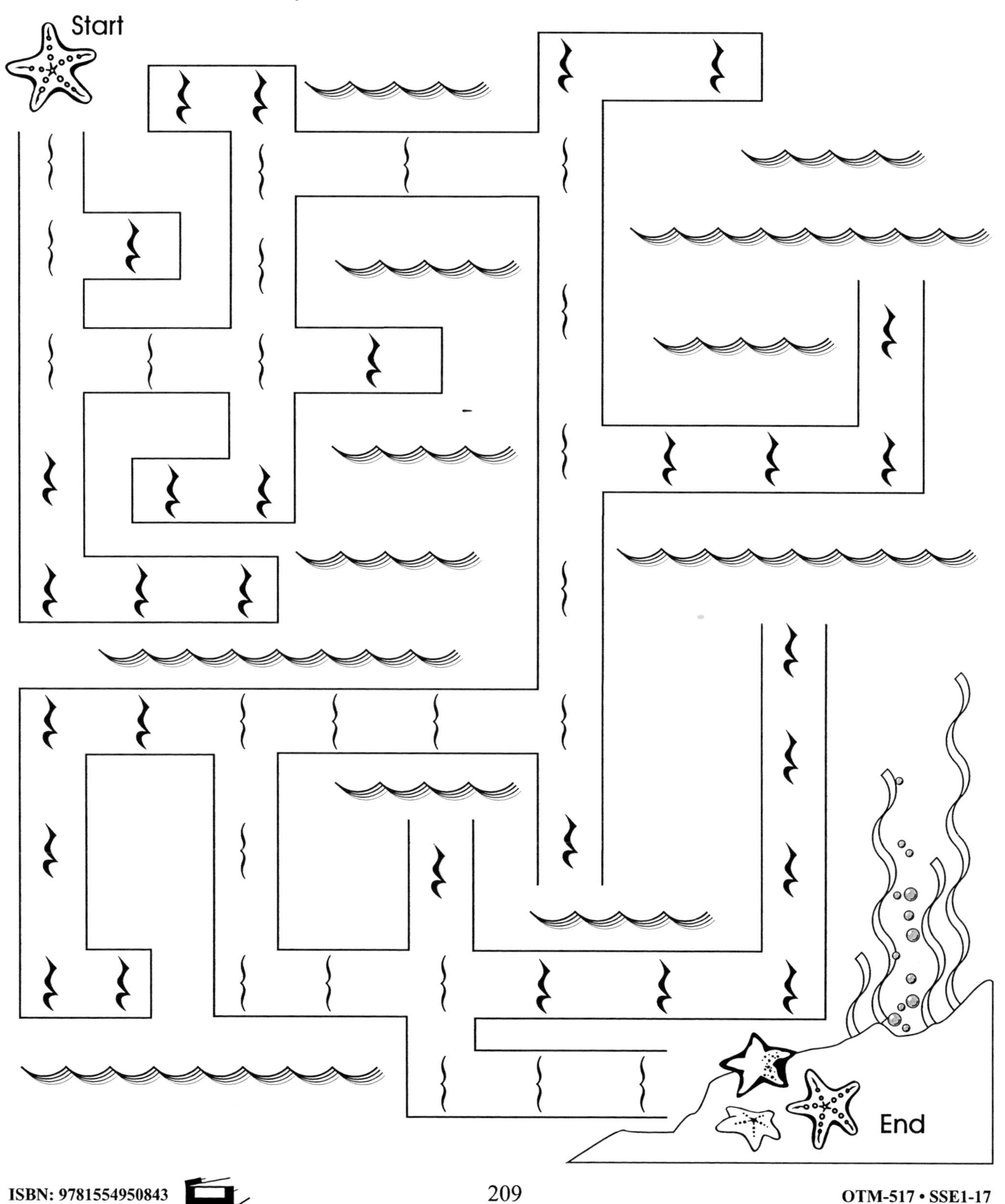

# Musical Games

## Game #1 - Spinner Quest

**Game Pieces:**

a spinner, the question and answer sheet, somewhere to score

**Preparations:**

1. The spinner needs to be assembled before playing. It is found on page 212.
2. This page with the large circle numbered 1 to 14 must be cut out and glued onto the pie plate.
3. The spinner, which can be made from plastic, needs to be attached with a duo tang clip in the center. This spinner, which is shaped like an arrow, should be able to spin and point to the numbers which coincide with the question sheet.
4. Score cards are needed, or the score can be kept on the chalkboard.

**Playing the Game:**

1. This game can be played as a class or split into groups.
2. The first student spins.
3. The teacher then reads the corresponding question.
4. The group or individual must answer correctly for one point.
5. Individually, players are eliminated with a wrong answer. As a group, teams must reach a certain number of points to win.

## Game #2 - Musical Memory

1. This is a memory card game.
2. Pages 215 and 216 need to be photocopied, mounted on a sturdy backing, and cut to assemble the cards for the game.
3. The cards are then lined up face down in any order and player one turns over two random cards to try and match a pair.
4. If they don't match, the cards are returned face down and the next player takes a turn.
5. If a pair is matched, the pair is kept and they take an additional turn until they do not match a pair.
6. The player with the most pairs wins the game.
7. Do not include the old composer card for this game.

# Musical Games

## Game #3 - The Old Composer

1. The same cards, as in Game #2, are used for this game, including the Old Composer card.
2. Players are dealt all the cards.
3. Player #1 asks the player on the left for a card that he/she has in his/her hand and tries to get a matching pair. If the player does, the player goes again. If the player doesn't, the next player plays.
4. The pairs of cards are displayed in front of them and counted at the end.
5. The player with the most pairs wins the game.
6. The player left with the old composer card becomes "The Old Composer."
7. Make sure if you are adding additional copies of the cards that you have only one old composer card so there isn't a matching pair.

## Game #4 - Go Rest

1. This is also a card game, using the cards with the rests.
2. They also need to be assembled.
3. The object of the game is to get four of the same cards for a set which gives one point.
4. Four copies of page 217 are needed for a full deck of cards.
5. Players are dealt seven cards.
6. The rest of the cards are put in the middle face down, in a pile.
7. The first player asks the player on the left for a certain card. The player must give all of the cards in his/her hand that add up to the number of rests asked for.
8. If the player is successful, he/she can ask for a different one until the player asked doesn't have that card and says "Go Rest."
9. Player one takes a card from the middle and it is player two's turn.
10. When four of the same cards are collected, the set is placed down in front of the player.
11. The highest number of sets wins the game.

## Suggestions

1. The games will teach the students to recognize music signs, instruments, and the value of a one beat rest.
2. You may want extra sets of cards because they tend to wear out after time. If the students are having problems recognizing the signs, you could also color code the same cards to make it easier.
3. If you are working in groups, you may want to have other materials such as reproducibles and worksheets available in case some games take longer than others to play.

# Spinner

GAME #1

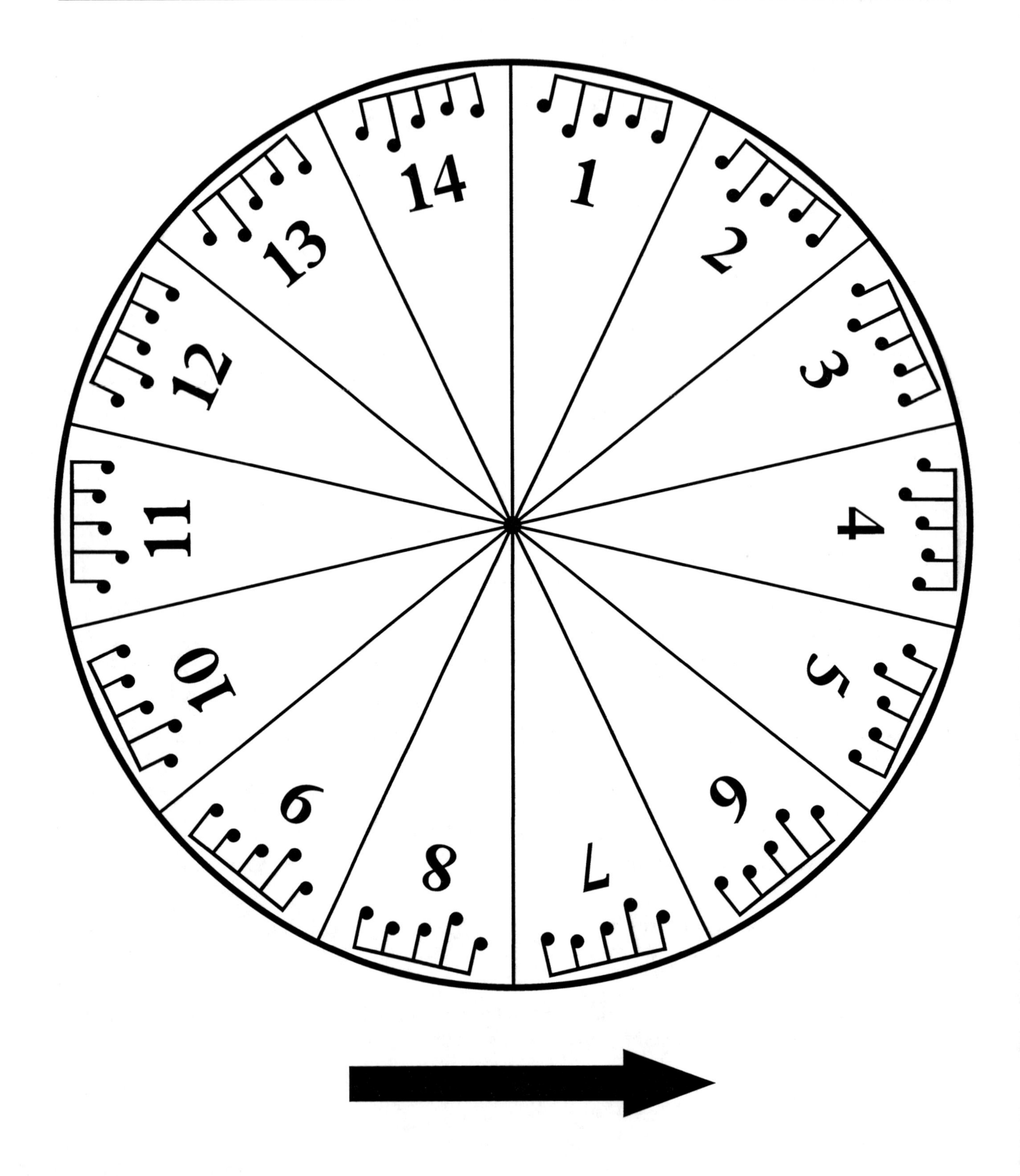


ISBN: 9781554950843

## Questions and Answers: Group A

1. What is the sign that holds the staff together with another staff? (the brace)
2. What does a three-beat note look like? (white with a dot)
3. What do you do when you see a repeat sign at the end of a song? (repeat the whole song)
4. What looks like a flute but is smaller? (a piccolo)
5. What does a clarinet use to make a sound? (a reed)
6. What is bigger and deeper in sound than an oboe? (a bassoon)
7. What is a woodwind instrument but is made of brass? (a saxophone)
8. What happened to Beethoven when he was in his twenties? (He went deaf.)
9. How would Beethoven conduct an orchestra? (He would jump all over.)
10. How old was Beethoven when he began to play the piano? (He was four years old.)
11. Why would no one marry Beethoven? (He was very moody.)
12. How do you play a woodwind instrument? (You blow through tubing with holes, Some of them are being opened and some of them are closed.)
13. Who wrote the music called “Ode to Joy?” (Beethoven did.)
14. Does a reed last as long as the instrument? (No)

### Questions and Answers: Group B

1. In singing, what comes after Re? (Mi)
2. What are the seven letters used in music? (A B C D E F G)
3. How many beats does a black note get? (one beat)
4. How many spaces are on a staff? (four)
5. What is the clef used for high notes? (the treble clef)
6. What is the clef used for low notes? (the bass clef)
7. What separates the music into sections? (the bar lines)
8. What is at the end of a song? (a double bar line)
9. What is a beat? (one tick of a clock or one tap of a stick)
10. How many beats does the rest that looks like a hat get? (2 beats)
11. How many lines are on a staff? (five)
12. How many beats would tick, tock, tick, tock be? (4 beats)
13. How many beats does the white note with a dot get? (three beats)
14. When you are resting, should you hear anything? (No)

# Cards

GAMES #2 & #3

# Cards



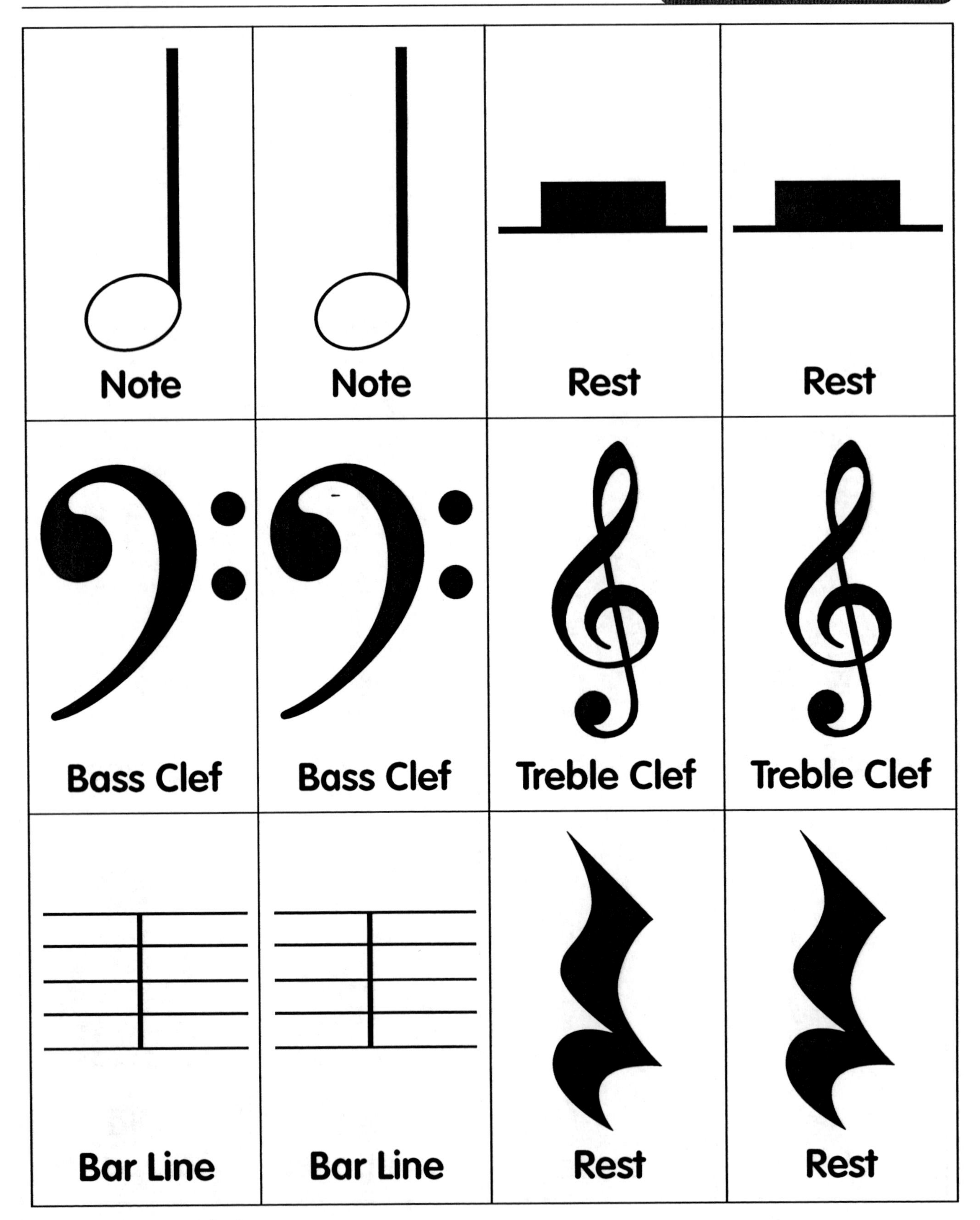
Note
Note
Rest
Rest
Bass Clef
Bass Clef
Treble Clef
Treble Clef
Bar Line
Bar Line
Rest
Rest

# Go Rest! Grade 3 Cards

GAME #4

Teacher Notes:

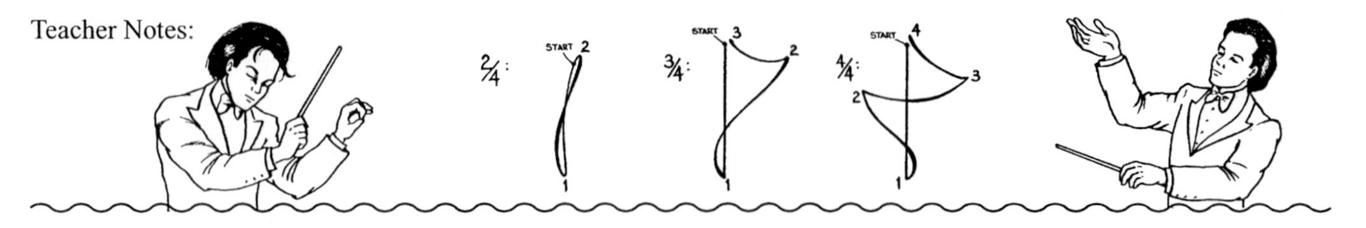


# Review Worksheets, Quiz, and Review Art

1. There are two worksheets of review facts found on pages 219 and 220. These will help the student review the musical signs learned before writing the Quiz. The two pages should be colored according to the code on the page. The music sign, the arrow, and the term should end up all being the same color.

2. The Quiz can be used as a test. It is found on page 221. The arrows are used so that the lines do not cross one another and you end up not knowing which line goes with which sign. You can also use a different color for each sign. The arrows would then not be necessary.
   The Quiz is out of ten. The first answer is an example and the students would get one right as a bonus.

3. The worksheets found on pages 222, and 223 are to be used to develop creative expression in written and drawn form.

4. The certificates on page 224 can be reproduced, filled out, and presented to each student in the classroom.

MORE REVIEW

Color the 3 beat sections black. Color each sign, matching word, and arrow the same color.



220

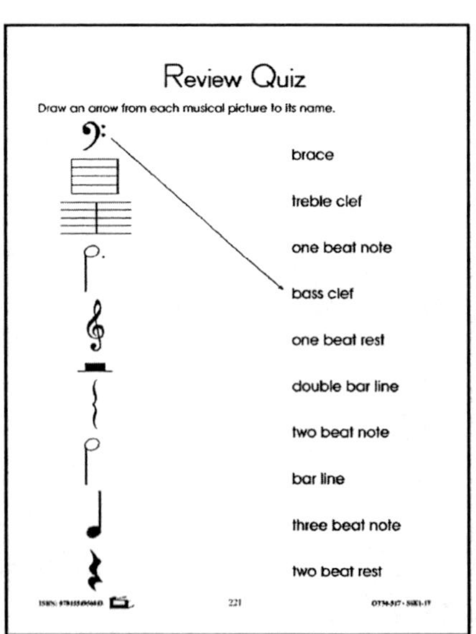
Review Quiz

Draw an arrow from each musical picture to its name.

brace
treble clef
one beat note
bass clef
one beat rest
double bar line
two beat note
bar line
three beat note
two beat rest

221

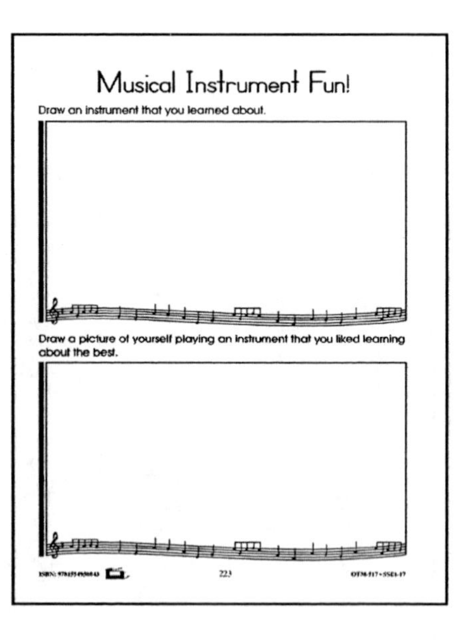
Musical Instrument Fun!

Draw an instrument that you learned about.

Draw a picture of yourself playing an instrument that you liked learning about the best.

223

# REVIEW FACTS

Color the 2 beat sections black. Color each sign, matching word, and arrow the same color.

# MORE REVIEW

Color the 3 beat sections black. Color each sign, matching word, and arrow the same color.

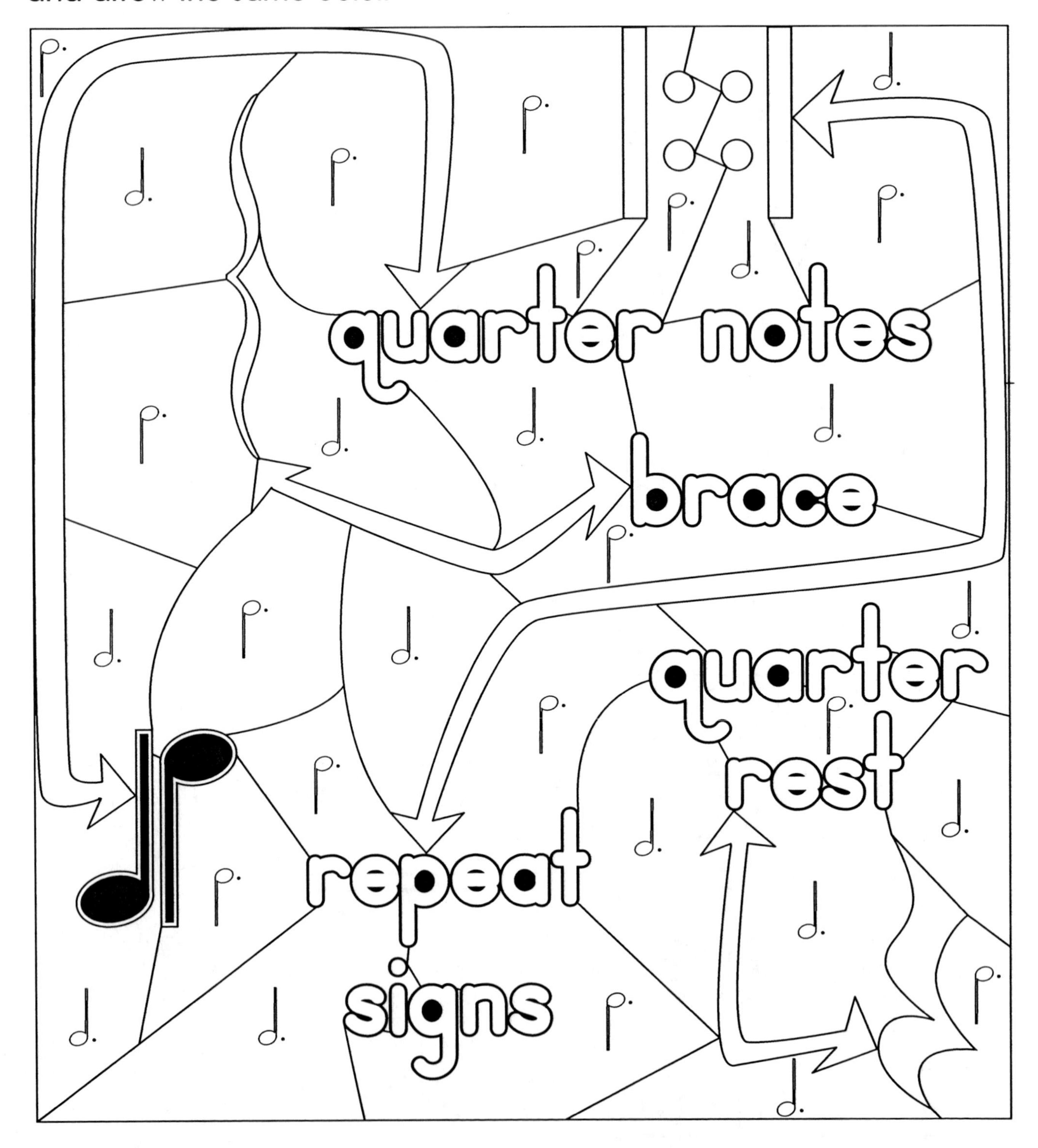

# Review Quiz

Draw an arrow from each musical picture to its name.

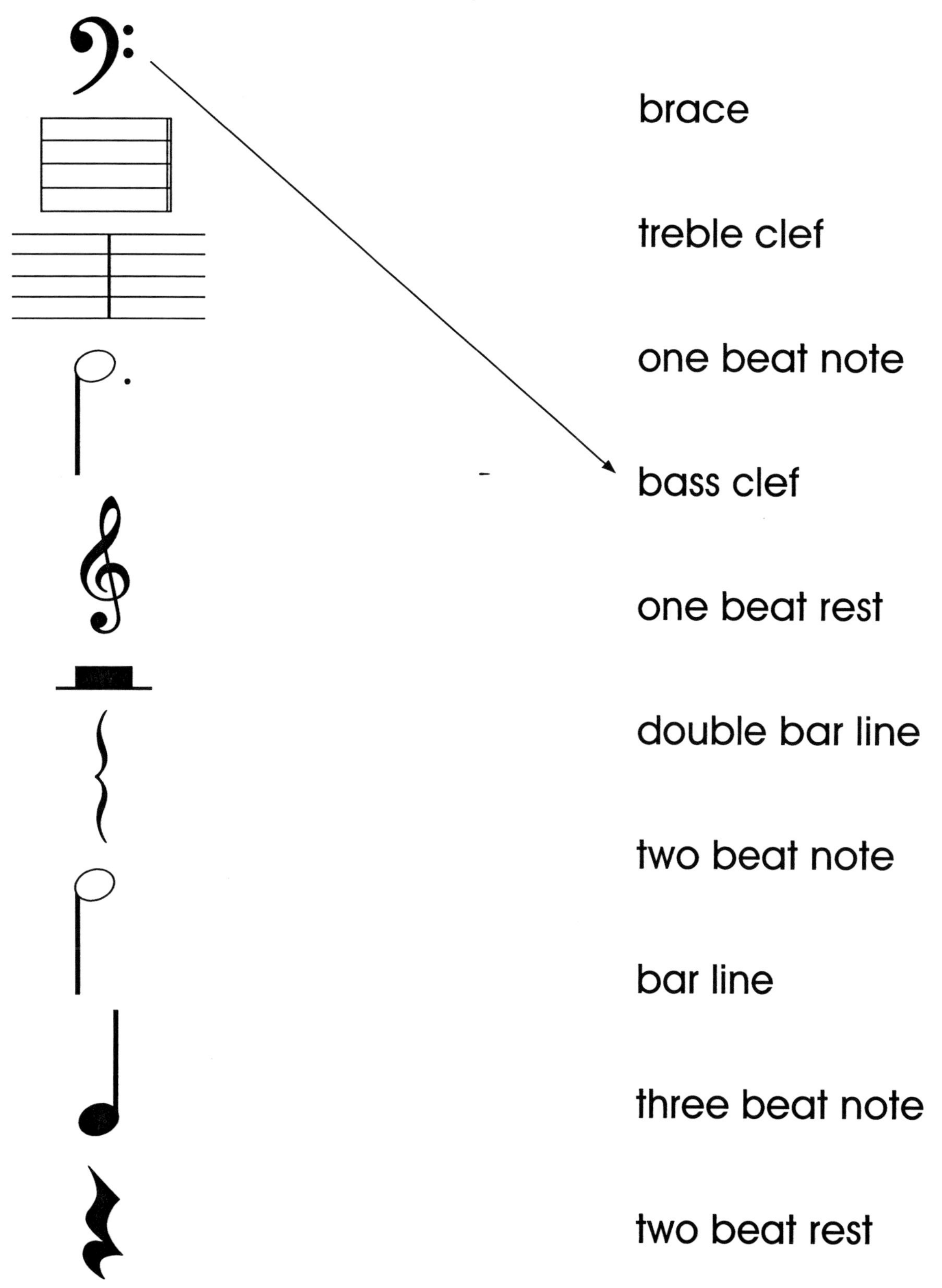

# Music In My World

I heard music playing ________________________________________

I saw ________________________________________ playing music.

It was ________________________________________

In the shape box below draw a picture of a time when you heard or saw music being played.

ISBN: 9781554950843

# Musical Instrument Fun!

Draw an instrument that you learned about.

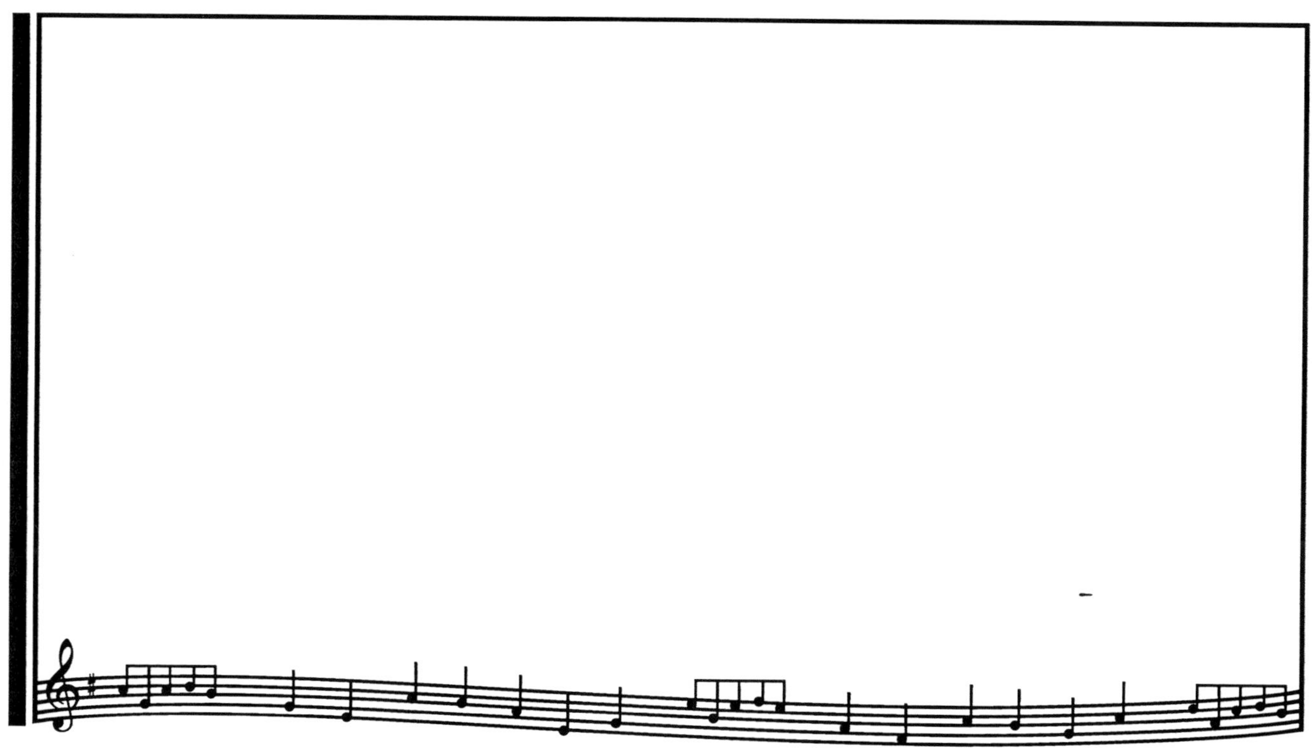

Draw a picture of yourself playing an instrument that you liked learning about the best.

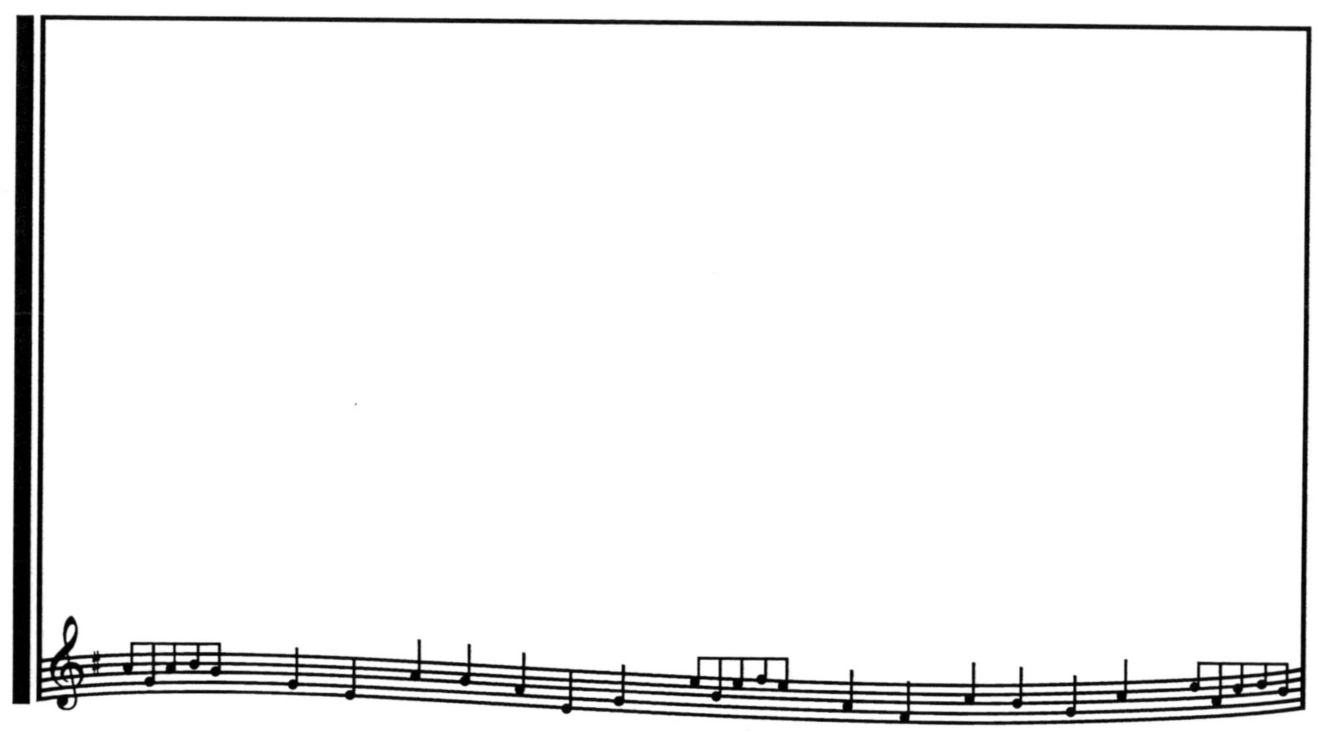

This is to certify that ____________________

has completed

**GRADE ______ MUSIC IS FUN.**

Teacher's Signature: ____________________

This is to certify that ____________________

has completed

**GRADE ______ MUSIC IS FUN.**

Teacher's Signature: ____________________